Helping Yourself
with Psychiatry

A Practical Guide to

Wiser and Healthier Living

by

FRANK S. CAPRIO, M. D.

1957

PRENTICE-HALL, INC. • *Englewood Cliffs, N. J.*

PRINTED IN THE UNITED STATES OF AMERICA

07307

To You

Most of us go through life knowing only half of ourselves, so we use only half our resources of ability and confidence and happiness. Great areas of strength remain hidden. We suffer — because we are strangers to ourselves.

My grateful thanks to:

The late Douglas Lurton who had given me permission to use material previously published in the form of articles in *Your Life* and other magazines of which he was editor.

Various staff members of Prentice-Hall who so kindly assisted me in the final preparation of the manuscript.

Contents

▄▄▄

What Psychiatry Can Do For You

What Psychiatry Can Do For You

▪▪

- ## *What Kind of Person Are You?*

Did it ever occur to you to ask yourself:

- What sort of person am I?
- Why do I think and behave as I do?
- What are my blind-spots, weaknesses and personality-shortcomings, which I either fail to recognize or refuse to acknowledge?
- How is my health affected by emotional frustrations of everyday life?
- Do I have a distorted sense of values?
- Am I immature in my attitude toward sex, love, people, and life in general?
- What subconscious motivations lie behind my prejudices and hatreds?
- Am I too egocentric or oversensitive?
- Do I blame others for my own failures?
- Am I putting forth a sincere effort to grow and improve?
- What is my ultimate goal in life?

If you are honest with your self-appraisal answers, you may discover the reason for many of your difficulties.

Do you realize that if you devoted a short time each day to analyzing your faults and correcting them, utilizing the advantages of *bibliotherapy* (therapeutic benefit obtained through reading self-help books) you could become a *completely new person.* It can be done. It merely requires a bit of *self-knowledge, self-discipline,* and a *determination* to acquire a new set of thinking habits.

• *The* Willingness *to be* Helped *is* Half *the Battle*

Everyone, and that means *everyone,* can stand some *self-improvement.* This book was written to serve as a guide to emotional well-being through self-analysis. It is intended to help you to help yourself—to assist you in solving your personal problems wisely—to uncover the motives behind your behavior—to budget your nervous energy—to become master of your emotions—to increase your efficiency—to enjoy life more fully.

In many instances the psychiatrist is credited with curing his patient. Actually, the *patient cures himself.* The psychiatrist acts as a *counselor* and *teacher,* enabling the patient to achieve self-understanding. Without the patient's cooperation, a cure cannot be effected.

The preservation of one's mental health is both a *science* and an *art* that can be taught to those who wish to learn. To learn you cannot be resistive to changing your pattern of thinking; you must be receptive to constructive suggestions regarding remedies for those faulty adjustments to everyday problems of life.

If you develop a *willingness to be helped,* acknowledge the *need to understand yourself,* and take a *personal inventory* of yourself as well as exert a *determined effort to change for the better,* your days ahead will become most rewarding.

• *You Can Help Yourself*

It is estimated that there are approximately 14,000,000 persons in the U. S. A. suffering from emotional conflicts who could benefit from the help of a psychiatrist. If you are one of these half-alive 14,000,000, it should be comforting for you to know that you are capable of helping yourself—of changing your thinking and way of life. You may discover that those health-ailments that are so distressing are *psychosomatic* (brought on by emotional frustration) and that *you can't cure emotional ills with pills.*

Emotionally induced illness, (a term used by Dr. John

Schindler, author of the bestseller *How to Live 365 Days a Year*) can be averted. You need only to learn and understand the origin and psychology of your emotional conflicts, your fears and anxieties and their relationship to your physical health. The intelligent application of this knowledge should enable you to *be your own psychiatrist,* with the reservation of course, that if your particular difficulty is too deep-seated you will exercise wise judgment by seeking the guidance of a competent specialist.

• *Knowledge is Power*

Some people are of the opinion that "A little knowledge is a dangerous thing." They claim that too much introspection gained from reading self-help literature only serves to increase one's original anxieties. They remind themselves of the proverbial saying: "Where ignorance is bliss, it is folly to be wise."

But isn't it a fact that the driving of an automobile can prove dangerous if the driver is intoxicated, irresponsible, or reckless? Would that justify stopping the manufacturing of automobiles? Just as atomic energy contains the world's greatest potential for advances in the field of medicine and science, we are also painfully aware that it represents the world's most devastating force. However, it is not atomic energy per se, but the use we make of it that determines its good or harmful potentialities. Likewise, it is unintelligent to suppress scientific knowledge because a few hysterics make wrong use of what they learn.

There are persons, for example, who advocate the suppression of books dealing with sexual enlightenment. Psychiatrists have found that these over-defensive individuals suffer from *moral hypocrisy.* Their prudery or *pseudo-morality* represents an unconscious defense mechanism against their own unresolved sexual conflicts. They fear that sex-education books might enhance their feelings of guilt. As Dr. Ernest Jones, a world-renowned psychoanalyst expressed it: "It is people with secret attractions to various temptations who busy themselves most with removing these temptations from other people;

really they are defending themselves under the pretext of defending others, because at heart they feel their own weaknesses."

This perhaps explains why Sigmund Freud met with such severe criticism when he attempted to expose the secrets of the unconscious—our instinctive cravings that we tend to *repress*.

In a letter to a young writer (Bruno Goetz), Freud wrote:

> My purpose is to help as well as I can the many people who today live internally in hell. Not in some hereafter but here on earth most people live in hell. . . . My scientific findings, my theories and methods aim at making them conscious of this hell so that they will be able to free themselves from it.

Ignorance does damage. Knowledge is power; it banishes fear. Fear makes you run away from life. Self-understanding gives you a foundation for well-balanced living.

• *What is the Role of the Psychiatrist?*

There are many uninformed people today who harbor the misconception that a psychiatrist is one who treats only persons who are "neurotic." For their benefit, let me say that a psychiatrist in private practice is a physician who specializes in the treatment of various kinds of nervous and mental disorders. He is a specialist who is qualified to analyze and understand the emotional frustrations of everyday life in relation to people's health. He is capable of guiding and assisting people with their individual problems. He investigates the emotional implications of symptoms for patients of other physicians, patients who come to be treated for physical ailments, but whose difficulties prove to be primarily emotional and mental. It might be said that a psychiatrist is one who studies his patient's joys and sorrows, his hopes and fears, and who is convinced that it is just as important to know what sort of *patient* has a disease as it is to know what sort of *disease* a patient has.

• *Types of Illnesses Treated by the Psychiatrist*

Among the many conditions that the average psychiatrist encounters in private practice are personality-maladjustments, phobias and morbid fears, marital troubles, sexual problems, mental depression, alcoholism, feeling of inferiority and inadequacy, health-complaints that fail to respond to medication, "nervous breakdowns," and psychoses.

The duration of treatment, just as in physical disturbances, depends upon each individual case. Some conditions respond to relatively short treatment.

• *Psychiatry Today is an* Indispensable *Specialty*

It would be unfortunate indeed if the reader gathered from the contents of this book the erroneous impression that psychiatry is a superfluous specialty, that psychoanalysis is a luxury that only the rich can afford. As a practicing psychiatrist myself, I am only too well aware of the advantages of a person receiving professional help. We all know of the thousands who are urgently in need of the services of a psychiatrist because of their failure to sustain a happy life.

• *Exactly What Happens in a Psychiatrist's Office?*

One of the first things a psychiatrist does is to carefully scrutinize his new patient. This initial interview is an exceedingly important one, because it gives the psychiatrist an opportunity to arrive at a tentative *diagnostic evaluation* of his patient. In a good many instances his first impression turns out to be a correct one. He quickly decides whether his patient is suffering from a deepseated neurosis, or is merely a victim of a situational-frustration that is much simpler to correct.

The psychiatrist further estimates whether the patient is likely to respond favorably to treatment or is apt to prove *resistive* and *uncooperative*. He bases his deductions on the study of his patient's general appearance, personality characteristics, and behavior in the office. He notes whether the patient comes alone or is accompanied by a close relative or friend; whether he is thin or fat; wears glasses or is hard of hearing; has good or bad posture; looks sad or mad; is agitated, relaxed, or indifferent. He listens attentively to what the patient has to say and how he says it; notes whether he is rational or irrational in his reasoning, and whether or not he displays any insight into the nature of his illness.

At the conclusion of the consultation, he gives the patient the benefit of his professional opinion, discusses the fee-arrangement and works out a suitable program of treatment.

If the psychiatrist is a *psychoanalyst* (one who has been analyzed himself and has had training in this particular method of treatment) he will have his patient lie on the couch for his subsequent sessions. The object of the couch is to have the patient relax physically. It has the added advantage of enabling the patient to concentrate on what he wants to talk about with less distraction. Women patients, especially, experience less embarrassment if they can reveal their intimate past without having to look at the psychoanalyst. This method also benefits the analyst, because he too is able to relax and evaluate what he hears and is spared the strain of a face-to-face interview. Not all psychiatrists are psychoanalysts. Therefore many patients who go to a psychiatrist do not have their sessions on a couch.

Incidentally, persons who most need guidance and re-education often times are most reluctant to consult a psychiatrist. Their ego-sensitivity (particularly the male sex) makes them self-conscious about admitting to themselves their need for one. One explanation lies in the fact that they are afraid of what they may learn about themselves.

What the psychiatrist tells a patient in the way of helping him to better understand his difficulties is spoken of as *Psychotherapy*.

The term is derived from the words "psyche" meaning *mind* and "therapy" meaning *treatment*. Psychotherapy therefore can be defined as a technique of treatment used by a psychiatrist to influence and improve his patient's thinking about (1) himself (motivations behind his present and past behavior), (2) his health (helping him to differentiate between those symptoms that are *physical* in origin and those that are *psychogenic* or neurotic in origin), (3) his social environment (attitude toward people), and (4) his philosophy of life. Psychotherapy (insight-therapy) in a way can be considered *Personality-therapy.*

In the course of a number of *psychotherapy-sessions* the patient begins to find himself. He learns for the first time things he has never understood about himself. In this respect we say that being psychoanalyzed is like *looking in a mirror* and seeing yourself for the first time—as you really are.

• *Patients Cure Themselves*

Whenever the relative of a new patient asks me during the initial interview, if I can guarantee a "cure," I make it a point to tell him that no psychiatrist cures anyone.

The psychiatrist merely acts as a *teacher* and *guide.* He provides his patient with a road map pointing out the dangerous detours he expects them to avoid and the *direction* they are to go. He gives the patient the opportunity of analyzing himself for the first time. This inner new knowledge of himself brought about via self-analysis, together with the moral support of the psychiatrist, enables the patient to change for the better, ridding himself of his many fears and emotional conflicts. Eventually every patient has to learn to be his own psychiatrist.

That many people are able to analyze their own emotional problems to advantage is borne out in "Self-Mastery Through Psychoanalysis" * by William J. Fielding, who writes:

> Psychoanalysis and particularly autopsychoanalysis, i.e., training ourselves to tap and draw upon the wealth of the Unconscious, is not only conducive to mental and psychic upbuilding but forms a valuable method of utilizing and developing our latent possibilities. It is a form of self-education that cannot be acquired in any other way.
>
> The process of going over and over and re-examining our experiences until we thoroughly understand

* Eton Books, Inc. N.Y. 1952

their significance is part of the practice of self-analysis. This, of course, does not imply that one should pick out certain sordid memories and dwell on them, which is bound to leave a morbid state of mind that may in time become a fixed mental condition. On the contrary, the habit of analyzing our experiences (if done with something of a detached, objective attitude, which may be acquired) is productive of far-reaching intellectual results.

• Can Habit-Patterns be Changed?

I have been asked innumerable times, by friends as well as patients, "How can you make people *different?*" as if they were implying that you cannot change the spots on a leopard. They have the notion that everyone's basic personality remains the same. Some patients tell me: "Doctor, I'm afraid I'm too old to change. I should have come to you years ago." Others regard any change in personality as merely a temporary *surface-improvement* and believe that ultimately the person will revert back to his original behavior patterns. This might hold true for some. However, it is a common consensus of opinion among psychiatrists that people *can* be changed and reeducated to the point of manifesting evidence of continuous improvement. The late Karen Horney, the famous psychoanalyst, made public years ago her opinion that most persons can change for the better if they determine to do so. As a matter of fact, one of her published works dealt with a patient who overcame her personality difficulties via *self-analysis*.

There are pessimists who contend that behavior patterns become set. If this were true, the specialty of psychoanalysis would never have survived. The evidence is to the contrary—most of us can become well-integrated individuals. A person who develops insight into the unconscious attitudes that motivate him can train himself to substitute certain *healthful habits* of thinking and reacting in place of those that brought him unhappiness. He finds that he can even extend this new evaluation of himself in terms of his past experiences, to a deeper psychological appreciation of why other people think and act as they do.

• *Why* Do *People Behave as They Do?*

Various theories have been advanced attempting to explain the enigma of the many variations in human behavior. Every psychiatrist at one time or another, has been asked these challenging questions:

- What makes a person *mal-adjusted?*
- Is *heredity* to blame?
- Why are some people so difficult to get along with?
- Why do people react *differently* to personal misfortunes?
- Are *parents* to blame for juvenile delinquency?
- Why do some people drink to excess or take drugs?
- What can the high divorce rate (400,000 a year) be attributed to?
- Is jealousy a sign of love?
- Why do so many people today use *tranquillizer* pills, and are they healthful or harmful?
- Are homosexuals *born* that way?
- Can criminals be rehabilitated?
- What causes a person to hate other people?
- What causes wars?
- What makes a person an atheist?

Freud believed that neurotic behavior stemmed from sexual conflicts. Alfred Adler explained human behavior with his *will-to-power* theory, claiming that every human being strives to overcompensate in one way or another for his basic feelings of inferiority. Carl Jung emphasized man's need for religion.

Despite the many different schools of thought, we all find ourselves living under a common sky in a troubled world, one in which everyone is struggling to survive *physically, economically* and *emotionally.*

It has been my personal contention for many years that man's basic frustration lies in the fact that he is *born to feel emotionally insecure.* Man is *born afraid, lives afraid,* and *dies afraid.* In this respect all human beings share an inevitable sense of *insecurity* constantly exposed to the threats of premature death. We seek comfort and consolation in religion and the promise of immortality. However, whenever our self-preservation is threatened in any way, we have a compulsive tendency to react with *fear.* This in turn gives rise to excessive self-preservation, resulting in our becoming neurotically *defensive* and *hostile.*

It would seem to me that people behave as they do because of *fear*—the common denominator of all behavior. Unable to understand and control this inner fear, which in most instances is *unconscious,* we become victims of various manifestations of *selfishness.* We think and act *defensively.*

By learning to understand ourselves in relation to our unconscious we are better able to control our fears and anxieties, to develop a greater incentive to be *unselfish,* and ultimately to achieve the peace of mind we are all seeking.

• *Where to Start "Being Your Own Psychiatrist"*

Psychoanalysts are required to be analyzed themselves, before they can analyze others. They must learn to evaluate their own deficiencies, eliminate them, and show evidence that they themselves are stable, well-integrated, and free from emotional conflicts. It would be ironical for a patient to accept advice from a psychiatrist who needs a little advice himself.

Isn't it just as logical to assume that if you are at odds with yourself you cannot hope to get along with others. Unhappiness is not only *habit-forming,* it is also *contagious.*

Therefore start with the conviction that until you achieve *self-understanding* and appreciate the *root-cause* of your *own personal-unhappiness* you cannot be harmonious company for others.

Decide *right now,* not tomorrow, that you are going to surrender forever that "I can't" attitude—that you are going to find out the *truth* about yourself and that while reading this book you are going to do some real *mental housecleaning.*

Believe that you *can* improve and that you will be ultimately *happier* for it.

• *The Purpose of the Book*

It is my sincere hope that our twenty-two sessions of *psychotherapy*, covering principles of personal mental hygiene, (1) will enable you to develop a deeper understanding of yourself and others, (2) will help you achieve greater self-reliance, and (3) will convince you that one of your *greatest* triumphs in life is the conquest of that inner-self that should teach you and others—*it is better to love than to hate*.

Lucy Freeman in her book *Hope For The Troubled* emphasized this very need for *tolerance, self-understanding*, and *love*, which she expressed so effectively as follows:

> No one wants to hate if he is able to love. No one wants to be unhappy, once convinced of a better way of living. No one is to blame for feeling troubled.
>
> If we are to help ourselves and others, we must first lose our fear of troubled feelings. We must know that a man is no more responsible for what makes him unhappy than for the virus that causes polio. Both are beyond his control.
>
> We cannot blame a helpless baby for being afraid because he does not receive love. Nor can we blame parents who themselves never knew love and so cannot give what they do not know.
>
> Instead of punishing men for their fear, can we know they seek love? Can we know that they strive for gain and glory or may murder—all in a vain attempt to get love?
>
> If we can, we will be able to help ourselves, our country, and the world to greater happiness and peace.

If this book has done nothing else but make the general public more psychiatry-minded in a healthy way ... if it has given those presently under the care of a psychiatrist the kind of insight that would tend to make them *less resistive* to treatment, if it has made the many who are urgently in need of professional advice and guidance *more amenable* to the idea of seeking help when necessary—this book will have served its purpose.

• *In Conclusion*

It is my added hope that those of you who have been *enlightened* via these informal sessions will be more inclined to be *kind* and *sympathetic* toward others who need so much to feel *loved* and *wanted*. In this respect, you are contributing in no small way to the overall goal of *preventive psychiatry*— the *prevention of needless unhappiness for yourself and others.*

Helping Yourself
with Psychiatry

$\mathcal{S}$ession 1.

Your Mind and How
It Functions

• *The Human Mind*

The average person finds it difficult to *control* what he has never been able to understand—the *workings of his own mind*. When you stop to think of it, *what is environment*, be it good or bad, but the *reflection* of *man's thinking*, the creation of his own Hell or Heaven through the action of his own mind.

You might ask, if the ills of civilization have been caused by man's inability to comprehend the motives that lie behind his destructive behavior, why haven't we done something about it in all the years that have gone by? The answer is that we *have*, but our job is only *half* done.

• *The Influence of Religion*

The perpetuation of many religions throughout the world is sufficient proof of man's attempt to influence social behavior in the right direction. *Religion* constitutes a form of *social discipline*.

However, man needs more than a promise of immortality

1

for obeying the Ten Commandments. Despite his faith in a Divine Power, man continues to commit crimes against humanity. We see ample evidence of this every day.

Psychiatrists believe they have found a reason why religion alone has been impotent to prevent wars, much less cure the individual of his mental ills.

• *The Need to Understand the* **Unconscious**

Up until 50 years ago we knew little about the *negative* side of man's nature. Psychoanalysis discovered that the solution to the enigma of human behavior lies neither in the study of *what* man does, nor in the attempt to convince him that it pays to be good, but rather in the desire to have him understand *why* he behaves as he does.

Today, more of us are convinced that abnormal behavior is an *illness* of the mind, a personality-sickness. So much so, that religion for the first time is turning to psychiatry for cooperation. The success of Norman Vincent Peale's *The Power Of Positive Thinking* [1] and Joshua Liebman's *Peace Of Mind* [2] are proof of the public's desire for a deeper psychological understanding of our emotional conflicts, in addition to its need for spiritual comfort through forgiveness.

• *The Three Parts of the Mind*

We need to evaluate properly the nature of our basic instincts and appetites in order that we may be better equipped to *control* them. The world, in this respect, is indebted to Sigmund Freud, the discoverer of Psychoanalysis, for in a sense he has been the first to X-Ray successfully the human mind and describe for us its complicated workings.

According to his theory, the mind consists of three parts:

1. *The Unconscious*
2. *The Conscious*
3. *The Conscience*

---

[1] Norman Vincent Peale, *The Power of Positive Thinking.* Englewood Cliffs, N. J.: Prentice-Hall, Inc., 1951.

[2] Joshua Liebman, *Peace of Mind.* New York: Simon and Schuster, 1946.

Freud gave these three parts of the mind specific technical names. He called the Unconscious, the *Id;* the Conscious, the *Ego;* and the Conscience, the *Super-Ego.*

• *The House That Freud Built*

If we think of the mind as a small house, we might say that the *unconscious* represents the "basement" or "cellar"; the *conscious,* the main floor where we do the actual living and entertaining; and the *conscience*—sometimes called the "moral censor" or "policeman"—the "attic." Now it is logical to assume that a cellar is never as clean or as orderly as the upstairs. In the majority of homes the cellar becomes the storage place for a lot of odds and ends and at the same time houses the fuel system of the house.

• *What You Need to Know About the Unconscious*

The *unconscious* is the storehouse of our primitive impulses. Sometimes it merely takes an excuse to justify to ourselves their expression—such alibis as bad heredity, poverty, physical handicaps, marital frustrations, and so on.

Most of our destructive tendencies are locked up in this "basement" of our mind. When we unlatch the cellar door and allow one of these imprisoned-impulses to escape, society suffers the consequences. Someone is killed, a bank is robbed, or some innocent girl is raped.

It is not always that serious. Most of us are not so rash as to deliberately allow our unbridled impulses such free expression. Instead we repress those desires that are socially objectionable. However, when the struggle to repress them becomes too great, to a point when these trouble-making impulses threaten to break loose, we become emotionally ill. Neurotic symtoms (headaches, nervous indigestion, insomnia, and so forth) come to our rescue, by acting as a *defense* against doing what is wrong. For example, I found among some of my patients that a fear of insanity was actually a disguised fear of committing some antisocial act.

• *Your Sexual Thermostat*

The sexual instinct present in every human being is represented by the furnace, also found in the "basement." But sex energy, like heat, must be regulated by a thermostat. Some people never learn to adjust their *sexual thermostat* (what Freud calls the "Libido" or sexual hunger) to a *normal* temperature.

As a result they either let the fire go out and become cold, suffer discomfort from too much heat, or risk a boiler explosion through carelessness or abuse of some kind. This explains why so much unhappiness can be traced to our failure to understand the nature of our sexual impulses.

• *Looking into the Past*

Many of us are afraid to explore or clean out the "cellars" of our mind for fear of what we might discover. In the cellar are stored all the memories of the past, all the things we have learned and experienced, ready for our use when we need them. The conscious must be kept clear of these past experiences until needed, in order to meet the new experiences of today and those anticipated for tomorrow. Life begins anew each day, but our approach to the new day and our attitude toward each new day's events are colored by our *past experiences* and how we reacted to them. The way we react today will largely depend upon our reactions of the past. Consciously we are unaware of the influence of the unconscious, although we ask ourselves, "Now, what made me do that? What made me act so foolishly?"

• *Your Personality Is Influenced by the Unconscious*

Habitual ways of acting are acquired throughout life in order to relieve consciousness of the burden of decision. We learn to walk, to bathe and dress, to eat, all without conscious direction. In the same manner we acquire habits of thinking. If we have learned to be kind and polite, to accept little hurts and upsets with a smile or shrug, to look on the bright side of life, then we tend to continue that course of acting and thinking throughout our lives.

If, on the other hand, we have habitually worn a chip on our shoulder, been quick to take offense, quick to retort unkindly, if we have been purposely rude and suspicious, disposed to cheat and lie, then our reactions will tend to be the same today. Knowing better, it will have been a constant struggle to react in a better way, to permit the *conscience* to *overcome* the *unconscious*. This daily conflict is not only a waste of energy but prevents the mind from attending to the higher things of every day life.

• *Everyone Has a Dual Personality*

Delving into the *unconscious* is considered by some, as equivalent to eating fruit from the Forbidden Tree of Life. But Freud, after 40 years of experience, mustered the courage to bite into the apple of knowledge and arrived at the conclusion that we all possess a *double personality*. He frankly admitted there is a Dr. Jekyll and Mr. Hyde in all of us, that behavior is determined by our ability to bring about a healthy *compromise* between these two opposing forces within us— the *unconscious* (which is always demanding the gratification of our selfish desires) and the moral *conscience* (which restricts and disciplines the impulse to do wrong).

• *An Actual Example of How the Unconscious Operates*

Perhaps I can illustrate my point by citing the case of Eleanor, who finds a purse with three hundred dollars in it. Her first impulse is to keep it. She considers herself lucky and dwells on all the things she can buy with the money. This is the *unconscious* working on her. The temptation to add to our sense of security at someone else's expense, is found in every one of us—a manifestation of the self-preservation instinct. But Eleanor finds herself tormented by her *conscience,* which whispers into her ear:

"You must return the purse to its rightful owner. His name

and address are plainly written on the identification card. How would you feel if you lost that much money? Can you be happy knowing that the loser of the purse is bound to suffer the consequences of his misfortune?"

However, despite these pangs of conscience, Eleanor decides to keep the purse and spends the money on clothes and luxuries, not knowing that there will be a price to pay for her dishonesty. Her sense of guilt begins to express itself in the form of migraine-headaches. But she never suspects any connection between her symptoms and the keeping of the purse. Ironically enough, she discovers that she has spent more than the amount she found, going from one doctor to another trying to get at the root-cause of her headaches. That is the way the mind works in thousands of cases of neurotic disorders.

• *Conscience-Sickness*

This *conscience* that was responsible for Eleanor's feelings of guilt resides in the "attic" of the mind. The *conscious self* is sandwiched in between the cellar and the attic. It is just as abnormal, however, for a person to live in the attic as it is for him to sleep in the cellar. There are many neurotics who suffer from a false guilt complex or what some have called *"conscience-sickness."* They take themselves too seriously, are overconscientious, and in extreme cases may even choose to become "ascetics," regarding the normal pleasures of life as "sinful." For instance, a morally over-sensitive woman who prefers to remain an old maid, rather than substitute an intelligent and healthy attitude toward love, sex, and marriage for fanatic prudery needs to be reeducated.

• *Your Unconscious Is Your Safe-Deposit Box*

It must not be thought that the *unconscious* is a storehouse for only the bad experiences of life. By no means is that true. Just as we have acquired good and bad habits of thinking and doing, we have stored away good and bad memories. The charm of good music is more than an appeal to our esthetic sense. It is a pathway back to pleasant memories of happy times with loved ones or friends. The feeling of well-being that comes with hearing music arises from a combination within us of happy memories, good resolutions, and lofty purposes. Occasionally music will bring back sad memories, regrets for wasted days and past mistakes, and we weep. If music brings to consciousness an appreciation of our short-comings and a resolution to find a better way of life, then music has been therapeutic.

What remains in the *unconscious* is similar to what remains in our *safe-deposit box*. There is nothing there we did not put there; there is nothing there we have not cherished. The impulses that have grown from the age-old instincts and emotions of the animal and that are unfitted for living in a civilized community, if allowed to endure, to rise up in our "bad moments" to torment us, will color our daily lives and distort our vision. To live peaceably with the world, we must first be able to live peaceably with ourselves. The constant *struggle* between the *conscience*, which makes for harmonious living, and an *unconscious* in which the repressed desires have become all-important, produces a feeling of emotional frustration and encourages our escape into neurotic illness.

• *Resolving Conflicts Between Your Conscience and the Unconscious*

Well-adjusted persons neither turn their back to the *un-conscious* nor do they thumb their nose at their *conscience*. They have learned not to become frightened when their mind indulges in mischievous thinking. They neither give expression to, nor repress their troublemaking cravings, but instead have learned to control them by *analyzing* and *understanding* them.

It is the up-and-down see-sawing of man's good and bad instincts that accounts for the fluctuations in individual and social behavior. It explains why history repeats itself with its cycles of wars and peace. Apparently Freud must have been inspired by the conviction that civilized man will never learn to live wisely until he has been able to *understand how his mind operates.* As Herbert Spencer once said: "It is the Mind that maketh good or ill, that maketh wretch or happy, rich or poor."

• *You Can Control Your Unconscious*

Here are some specific suggestions that may enable you to apply this new knowledge of *your mind and how it functions* to practical everyday living:

1. Remind yourself that we all possess certain instincts that we are obliged to *control*. Society expects us to muzzle our dog, particularly if it has a tendency to bite strangers. Why shouldn't we have to muzzle our *wild instincts* when they have a tendency to express themselves or get us into serious trouble?

2. Establish a *healthy compromise* between two extremes (the pleasure-seeking desires of your *unconscious* and the disciplinary demands of your moral *conscience*). Don't allow yourself to be dominated by your *unconscious*.

3. Accept the fact that every person's mind is capable of *mischievous* or *guilt-producing* thinking. Refuse to become alarmed or frightened by your fears and doubts.

4. Learn to substitute a *positive* thought for a *negative* one.

5. Remember it is not the things that happen to us that make or break us. It is our *mental reaction* to them that counts. Consequently it is better to be *logical* and *sensible* than to be *emotional* and *impractical*.

6. Making pleasure the *primary* purpose of living will increase your sense of guilt and cause further emotional conflicts.

7. Look back at the things that have happened to you and evaluate these long-forgotten experiences in terms of their unwholesome effect on your present emotional health. Bringing the skeleton out of the closet, becoming consciously aware of unconscious influences (those repressed

desires) is one way of eliminating your fears. Face your inner self.

8. Stop punishing yourself through neurotic health-ailments for feelings of guilt rising from the cellar of your mind. Divert the same energy toward cultivating some hobby that will serve as a *tension-reducer* for you.

9. Try to uncover the deeper motivating forces behind what you say and do. Self-insight gained through self-analysis will enable you to better understand your mind and how it functions.

10. Stabilize your emotional life.

11. Make *wisdom* your *partner* in all you think and do.

● *Techniques of Self-Analysis: The Autobiographical Method*

One specific way of getting to know about your *unconscious self* is the *autobiographical* method. Make an impersonal study in writing your life. Get a notebook and begin writing your autobiography. You'll be amazed when you're all through how much you'll learn about yourself. Start with what you know about your grandparents. Describe your mother, your father, the other members of the family and your relationship to each one. Continue with the description of your early home environment; the significant memories of your childhood and adolescence; the many experiences that left a deep impression on you; your educational achievements; the various positions you held; the disappointments in your life; the friends and enemies you have made; the good things that have happened to you; the kind of living habits and personality traits you have developed; your likes and dislikes; your past and present attitudes towards religion, people, and life in general; your sex life; and your plans for the future. Of course, you may have to be discreet, regarding what and how much to include in writing. You no doubt will have to take precautions, making sure that no one but yourself has access to your notebook. You can always destroy it after it has served its purpose.

My teacher, Dr. Wilhelm Stekel, had many of his patients

write their autobiographies. I tried it myself and found it well worth the time and effort.

I believe there lurks in the heart of most people a desire to write the story of their life. Be sure to include as you write what your emotional reactions were at the time to each event or "traumatic" experience. Be honest with yourself. Admit whatever mistakes you made and why you think you made them. The important thing is to arrive at some conclusion regarding why your life was what it was, your degree of responsibility for the many different situations in which you found yourself, and some of the concealed motivations that may account for your present patterns of thinking and behavior. It is not my intention to make an amateur psychiatrist out of you. Your deductions may only be "guesses," but I can guarantee you will know more about yourself than you ever did before.

In writing this book of your life, keep an imaginary mirror in front of you. Describe what you see *as you really are.*

● *The Questionnaire Method*

Another specific way of achieving greater self-understanding is the questionnaire method. Make your own list of questions pertaining to *you* and *your life's-problems.* Write out the answers to each question. Never tell yourself "I don't know." Your guess is better than no answer.

Start by answering the questions in the Introduction under the heading of "What Kind of a Person Are You?" Make up as many other questions as you can think of. This procedure should supplement your autobiography. Between these two methods alone, you are bound to have a better understanding of your unconscious self—that *other half* of yourself that has been a *stranger* to you.

● *The Free Association Method*

A third technique is the free-association method.

Psychiatry does its work by giving the patient an opportunity to *ventilate* his conflicts. Emotions that may be regarded as "psychological poisons," or vengeance, dissipate themselves through a process of *mental purging*. Psycho-analysts call this "catharsis"—the act of overcoming your conflicts by *talking* them out of your system. Each patient cures himself. The longer he talks, the more he divulges his inner self until, with the help of the psychiatrist, he is able to see and correct the root-cause of his trouble.

You can achieve the equivalent by writing, from time to time, whatever thoughts come to your mind. This is called "free-association," because one idea is unconsciously associated with some other thought which in turn leads to recalling something important in your life that has been repressed. It is a purging of your soul on paper (written catharsis). It also helps you dissipate unhealthy emotions.

You may recall having heard Mary Martin sing a song in *South Pacific*, "I'm Gonna Wash That Man Right Out of My Hair." You can *wash those frustrations right out of your life,* to paraphrase the thought, *by writing them out of your system.*

Many people unknowingly benefit by this technique when they write a lengthy, highly emotional letter to someone and tear it up the next day, having felt the better for it. I believe it was Abraham Lincoln who practiced and recommended this procedure. Letters that are abusive in content should never reach the mailbox. They should be dropped into the waste-basket instead.

Re-reading what you have *written* about your *frustrations* and *hates* will, in time, make them seem ridiculous. It is a method that will not only keep you from getting into difficulties but will enable you to attain a keener perspective of that inner you.

Session 2.

▰▰▰

Adopt a *Realistic*
Attitude Toward Life

• *Escapism: Flight from Reality*

Most of us would prefer to escape the painful realities of
life. This tendency to evade pain, either physical or mental,
is *normal*. After all, who likes things that are unpleasant?

Escapism is, therefore, a temptation common to all of us—
a desire to retreat, to escape from our responsibilities, and to
withdraw from our frustrations. Yet we can never really run
away from ourselves. We may not admit it, but many of us
are *unhappy* simply because we have decided we *"can't take
it."* When the going gets rough and our troubles bear down
too heavily on us, we all are tempted to resort to anything—
good or bad—that will help us to forget, to escape from the
distressing circumstances.

Henry was just such an *escapist,* a fugitive from reality. He
came from an unhappy home. His father was dominating,
aggressive, and abusive, as well as a poor provider. His mother
was tactless, nagged, and criticized endlessly. Life at home
became so unbearable that at the age of 16 he ran away and
never returned. Following his discharge from the service, he

secured a good position, married, and settled down. Unfortunately, his wife became involved with another man and the marriage ended in divorce. As a result he spent most of his time in pursuit of women, in drinking, gambling, coming in at all hours of the night, declaring that he was going to get his share of good times before he died.

Before he came to me he went to see his doctor complaining of insomnia. He was told it was a case of "nerves" due to his way of living. I discovered it was his sense of guilt that kept him awake. When he gave up his over-indulgence in wine, women, and song, stopped putting up a false front, and settled down to some serious planning for the future, his insomnia disappeared.

Henry was taught to realize that in trying to *escape* from his unhappiness by making a career of pleasure, he was resorting to a method that was least likely to succeed.

• *The Escapist Refuses to Face Reality*

The inability to endure physical inconvenience, such as hot or cold weather or hunger pains, or an inability to suffer disappointment and emotional frustration is common to escapists. They go to work only because they must in order to survive and are annoyed by every little happening of the day.

The normal person accepts physical and psychic discomforts of life, and accepts them philosophically as part of the business of everyday living. The escapist refuses to *face reality*.

Pain-producing situations are quite often psychological in origin. None of us react alike to frustrations. We have the Mary Smiths who commit suicide when jilted in love, the John Does, who take to drink when they lose their jobs, and the Bill Jones who go to pieces because of a bad marriage.

• *The Normal Person Faces Life Realistically, Courageously*

A *well-integrated* individual is *realistic* in his reaction to misfortune; he is prepared for hard luck, and courageously challenges Fate despite life's adversities. The *escapist* on the other hand, is *impractical* and fails to realize that life could be fascinating if he would only teach himself not to be a "poor sport"—to expect disappointments and not let them affect his mental and emotional health. He lives in the past and indulges in daydreams and fantasies of success.

He is *immature* about sex, love, and marriage and makes no effort to grow up, to improve. He has a weak chin. The first hard blow from Lady Fate and he's ready for the count.

Parents who condition their children to fear and dependency can expect them to be *emotionally weak* and unable to bear up under the frustrations of adult life. These dependent children are unable to make a satisfactory social and economic adjustment. They are forever seeking ways of running away from life's responsibilities. They very often hasten their own end. Unable to endure the adversities of life many of them *escape* in drink, drugs, or both, in gambling and philandering, or in neurotic illness. Why? Because their *Pain-Tolerance Quotient* (PTQ) is lower than normal.

• *The Living Dead*

Insanity is an example of *abnormal* withdrawal from reality. The insane withdraw into a dream-world where nothing outside can reach them. They divorce themselves from the turmoil of an outside world that they can no longer face. In this mental cave, they stare unthinking into space. They often refuse to eat. They shun all conversation. They want to be left alone. They adopt a negativistic attitude toward any suggestion of a cure. They enjoy the safety of their retreat.

Thus the insane have often been referred to as *the living dead*—as though they had committed *psychic suicide* and reincarnated themselves into a new world of *fantasy* and *unreality*. They are mental hermits, contentedly living in their vacuum. While others courageously struggle with life's responsibilities, they have made a private peace—an empty, shadowy peace. They have provided themselves with a way to protect their super-sensitive mental skins. Nothing can harm them now from without.

An inner voice whispers, "There is no solution to your problem . . . so just stop thinking about it. Retreat and live the rest of your life in a world of your own."

• *Escapism via Self-Destruction*

Suicide constitutes the most abnormal form of escapism— the act of a completely defeated mind. The normal person manages to find a better solution to the problem of financial reverses, incurable illness, disappointment in love, divorce, or failure to achieve a certain goal. The maladjusted add insult to injury by making others suffer for the problem they are unable to solve. False pride keeps them from revealing their innermost frustrations to anyone, and so they decide to escape via self-destruction.

• *Are You Living in an "Ivory Tower?"*

There are persons who, after achieving success, fame, or wealth, *retreat* from the world and isolate themselves in their private *ivory tower*. This is just another form of escapism. Success is to be *shared*. We owe it to ourselves and to others to become part of the world we live in, to give others the inspiration they need to succeed themselves.

• *You Must Live* Today

There are others who deprive themselves of normal pleasures, working and sacrificing for the day they are going to *retire.* I have known many such couples. They seldom entertain, live like social hermits, postpone their plans to travel, detach themselves from normal family ties, and fence themselves off from the rest of the world. In one instance, just at the time when such a couple was about to retire to their "dream-house" in sunny California, the wife died of a heart attack. The "dream-house" turned out to be just that— simply a *dream*-house.

Planning for the future is *sensible,* but you must also take into account the need for living *now—today.* There is no certainty about the future. Your *one* goal to enjoy life in *later years* may prove *too late*.

Living *today* means *not* living in the *past*. Yesterdays are like meals we have eaten; eating begins again *today*. That excellent meal last week cannot appease the hunger of today. Nor should the upsetting one of a month ago spoil the prospect of a delicious one tonight. Life goes one. The mistakes of the past are not the errors of today if we profited by our faults. The future with its problems and its joy is ahead. Lot's wife looked backward and she perished.

● *Normal Escapism is Necessary for Health and Happiness*

Fortunately there are many ways of making life less burdensome. There is a kind of running away that can be regarded as *normal*. We all need *mental rest*. A needed vacation gives one an opportunity to escape temporarily from daily responsibilities. The tired executive who makes time for fishing is to be commended. Whether it is an occasional highball, an intriguing detective story, an afternoon of landscape painting, a crossword puzzle, or a game of golf, they are all forms of *normal* escapism.

It matters little how you get your physical relaxation and mental distraction. It may be through sports, dancing, movies, or watching television. We all need something to relax us, some pleasant activity to take us away from our daily routine, our disturbing thoughts. This change we must have—this counter-balance is essential to good health. This does not mean of course, that we have to spend most of our life in a continuous pursuit of pleasure. A healthy amount of *normal escapism* can be mixed with the daily grind and make it less tedious. The well-adjusted person balances his work and worries with necessary recreational outlets.

● *Develop a Practical Philosophy of Life*

Let's face it. Life is a *battle*. It is a fight from start to finish—a struggle for survival from the womb to the grave.

With courage and patience we can be victorious despite the worst in circumstances. But only with *courage.*

Darwin was right when he said that life is a *survival of the fittest.* The weak succumb, the strong survive. Each of us makes his choice—conscious or unconscious—as to whether he will face life strongly or half-heartedly, whether he will advance to victory against the enemy or succumb to his weakness and retreat.

We live in a world of love, mystery, fear, and hate—a world of confusion and contradiction. We experience joys that stimulate us and sorrows that depress us. Heraclitus, the Greek philosopher, in his "law of opposites" proclaimed that man is doomed to a life of contradictory forces—love and hate, war and peace, living and dying, pain and pleasure. There is little you and I can do to change this world. It is the way we react to these dynamic forces that determine whether we are *normal* or *neurotic.*

• *Happiness is a Way of Thinking*

Everyone needs a *practical, workable,* philosophy of life, a *way of thinking* that makes living pleasant instead of painful. We need to develop a feeling of "I am"—of belonging—reminding ourselves that we are *glad* to be *alive.* If we develop strong ties with the world around us—the sun, the moon and the stars—if we are able to give love and are able to *accept* love, our own happiness will be assured. The capacity to enjoy living stems from a philosophy of life that is both *realistic* and *practical,* based on the principle that happiness to a large extent is an *attitude* of mind.

• *Develop a Philosophy for Living Joyfully*

While you are learning to be your own psychiatrist, become a *philosopher.* Remind yourself that rich or poor, we are all exposed to the same disappointments, threats, illnesses, storms, accidents, and wars. Your best defense is to build up an inner immunity against their effect on your morale. To accomplish this you must start with the conviction that you *can* survive physically and emotionally the painful realities of life. If others can do it, you can too, provided you do not take yourself too seriously. Acknowledge to yourself that it is your duty to your Creator, your family, and your friends to live out life bravely, despite besetting fears and discouragements.

Include in this philosophy a love of life, people, and your natural surroundings, and a faith in humanity. Above all be *realistic* in your *attitude* toward yourself, life, and the world about you.

• *Apply What You Learn*

Some of you are apt to say as patients often do, "But doctor, you haven't told me anything I didn't already know." Patients also claim that they have read many books of an inspirational nature and that none of them seemed to "do the trick," as if in some *magic* way the printed word should have made them feel better overnight.

I remind these patients that the mere reading of a self-help book will not guarantee to change you. Book knowledge per se can prove sterile. A college educated person may intellectually accept something to be true and yet continue to act in an immature way. It takes emotional *acceptance* of acquired knowledge as well as the *daily application of what you have learned.* Self-improvement books need to be *studied* and not read as a novel. For example, you may know and agree that it doesn't pay to worry, that it is best to assume an optimistic attitude toward everything. Consequently it isn't what you already know, its what you *forget* to *remind* yourself to do.

The practice of going to church on Sunday serves to remind us that there is more to life than just materialistic existence.

We all have this need to be *reminded* of some of the simple things we have read and learned that make for better living.

• *What to Keep in Mind*

1. Your problems can never be solved by running away from them.

2. However painful, assume new responsibilities willingly. It is the way of the weak (persons with a low PTQ) to let the *painful* realities of life overbalance appreciation of its *beauty* and *joyousness*. Make each day a challenge. Each successful encounter will give you added confidence.

3. To work without excessive complaining is vital to mental soundness.

4. The things that are most worthwhile in life are often the hardest to achieve.

5. Remind yourself that the many kinds of people (2,000,000,000) on this ball of earth (24,000 miles in circumference) that belongs to all of us— makes for a oneness of mankind.

6. Accept happiness as a *state of mind.*

7. Share your success and be a source of inspiration to those who need your guidance.

8. Start living today. Develop a feeling of "I am," of "I belong." Become part of the world you live in by participating, by making yourself useful and helpful to those in despair.

9. Adopt a *mature* attitude toward sex, love, and marriage. Don't expect everyone else to think and act as you do. Meet the world of other people halfway.

10. Stop living in a world of fantasy and day-dreaming.

11. Establish a healthy balance between work and play in your everyday program.

12. Be realistic about the past. You can't do anything about it except to profit from your mistakes. Convert your past misfortunes into assets.

13. Procrastination is a form of escapism. Don't put off until tomorrow what you can do today.

14. Make an agenda of the things you wish to accomplish each day. Use a small pocket notebook for this purpose. Carry it with you whereever you go.

Session 3.

▰▰▰

Self Analysis Through
Dream-Interpretation

● *The Ancient Art of Dream-Interpretation*

Dreams have always fascinated mankind. In fact, the art of deciphering dreams goes back to early antiquity. Evidence of man's attempt to evaluate his dreams can be found in ancient civilizations. Dreams were considered a bridge of communication between man and the supernatural. Primitive cultures regarded them as the language of demons and evil powers. Soothsayers believed that dreams could foretell one's future.

This prophetic power attributed to dreams inspired charlatans to exploit man's natural curiosity to know what the future holds for him. Clairvoyants later branched off into palmistry, tea leaf and sand readings, crystal-gazing, and astrological predictions. A remnant of this early dream-prophecy can be found in some of our popular dream books written by laymen.

It was not uncommon for people to believe that through dreams they were able to contact their divinity or communicate with the dead. Similarly, dreamers felt that they possessed unusual powers to "receive messages in their sleep" from the other world.

As time went on dreams were thought of as representing a struggle in man between two opposing forces—good and evil. This was not too far-fetched, for psychoanalysts discovered that dream-analysis is an indispensible technique in curing the neurotic. In dreams of neurotic patients we often find the *root-conflict* or unconscious motivations behind psychosomatic ailments. We also expose conflicts between the patient's *desires* and *repressions* (the struggle that takes place between the instinctual cravings of the *unconscious*—the Id— and the *moral censorship* of the Super-Ego).

● **Do Dreams Have Scientific Value?**

Yes. Today psychoanalysts say, "Tell us your dreams and we will *diagnose* your *troubles.*" Is this possible? Definitely, if one understands the method. The content of dreams has a scientific value. Modern psychiatry has learned that dreams can uncover the emotional conflicts responsible for nervous and mental illness.

Dreams reveal our secret wishes, our fears, loves, and hatreds. They betray our deepest feelings, for our *true self* comes to the surface when we dream.

In sleep we all manifest a *dual* character . . . a *Dr. Jekyll* and *Mr. Hyde* within us. The body sleeps, but the mind dreams. Our imagination runs wild in sleep. When we dream, our *inner self* is on the loose, giving us an opportunity to gratify those temptations that are *repressed* in the waking state.

The dream is the mirror of the dreamer's emotional life. Because we all differ in personality make-up, our dreams are naturally different.

Several years ago, I had occasion to analyze a total of 960 dreams of a patient whom I had never met. This particular research project was carried out in an attempt to determine whether or not it was possible to reconstruct the life-history of an anonymous patient through dream-interpretation alone.

The dream-survey consisted of information obtained exclusively from dream-material given to me by another psychoanalyst relative to the patient's family background, her relationship to each member of the family, childhood and early home environment, and other aspects of her life.

The published results of this experiment proved that her dreams were more revealing than the factual information she gave about herself to the other analyst.

Dreams reveal much about the *quality* of your emotions. It is some unsatisfied emotion that prompts you to dream about a particular situation. Regardless of how different the "scenery" of various dreams may be, they may have a lot in common because of a common emotional cause.

• Everyone Dreams

"But I never dream," you may say. It is as impossible to sleep without dreaming as it is to sleep without breathing. The mind is always at work. It is simply a matter of *remembering* your dreams. Why is it we cannot recollect our dreams? The truth of the matter is that we are sometimes *afraid* to remember them. When they are too horrible, or perhaps too pleasurable, nature comes to our rescue. The alarm clock goes off and memory of the wish-fulfillment of the dream fades away.

• Why Is It Important to Remember Your Dreams

What advantage is there in trying to recall your dreams? Why deliberately stir up a hornet's nest? Because in analyzing your dreams you are better able to appreciate those subconscious factors that disturb your life. It is these very factors that often explain the cause of your unhappiness and failure.

• Dreams Have Useful Functions

Just as every physical symptom in the sick individual serves a particular function for the organism, so if we assume that the dream is not a haphazard phenomenon, but a part of the orderly functioning of the mind, it, too, must have a function.

It would be difficult to believe that dreams are entirely meaningless and senseless. There is little doubt that the dream reflects, albeit in a grossly exaggerated form, the unfulfilled wishes and aspirations of the individual. It therefore has more than one function to perform or, to put it in another way, it can express its function in a great many different ways.

• Dreams Fulfill Our Wishes

The first function is that of *wish-fulfillment*. The most frequent emotional experience in the dream is a fervent wish for something to happen, successes to be obtained, or a goal to be reached. Quite often the emotion of the dream is that of anxiety, and it is interesting to note how frequent anxiety in dreams is followed by a large number of *psychosomatic reactions* such as palpitation of the heart, rising of the blood pressure, tremors, and sweating. Another frequent emotion in dreams is *anger*, which also may be accentuated by psychosomatic reactions.

To illustrate: John Smith is a very average, even mediocre, individual. He neither has the ability to achieve a higher position, nor does he have the energy to make the most of his capacities. He lives in a small community, a city of about 10,000, and looks with envy at the mayor of the city, inwardly anguished by the thought that he could never be mayor. How he would love it. He would give everything to be mayor, but his common sense tells him that there is no chance for him because he realizes that he has neither the ability nor anything else that such a position demands. But at night, when the slumber curtain falls, bitter reality disappears, and sleep removes the difficulties as if by a magic wand. Poor John Smith dreams that he was elected mayor of the city by an overwhelming majority. So great was his victory, so he dreams, that he receives congratulations from many nearby and even far away. He further dreams that so great was his success as a mayor, so productive and useful was his management that when next election came there was not even a doubt in anybody's mind that John Smith was going to be reelected.

Nobody wished to be his opponent, because they knew that they would be defeated.

This dream did not last very long, just a fleeting second, but it had a remarkable effect on John Smith. Next day he felt in good spirits. Even if merely in a dream, still he was mayor, and that was good to know. We see here that the dream performs a function of satisfying a much longed-for and unfulfilled wish. Everyone of us has *wish-fulfillment dreams*. They make us feel good, and in one respect they make life worth living—for what is important to us are not the hard realities of life but emotional satisfactions. And this is often derived from imagination and dreams than from actual accomplishments.

● *Wish-fulfillment Dreams Can Inspire Us*

Many a man has owed his success to his dreams. Wish-fulfillment dreams can act as an *inspiration*. Yet there is danger in them. There are those of us who over-compensate for feelings of inferiority by imagining ourselves at the top. We dream about unattainable goals, taking a shortcut to success. In reality, we are afraid to challenge obstacles that stand in our way. In fact, we are too lazy to make our dreams come true.

Worse, we begin to think the world is against us and refuse to recognize our abilities. We never really sit down and come to an honest evaluation of ourselves. We shrink from the hard task of thinking the matter through. We refuse to face the fact that what we need is a new attitude toward our circumstances, our work, and ourselves.

We are apt to substitute a world of fantasy, in which we substitute a dream-success and dream-happiness for one of reality. The gap between the roseate dream and reality makes the matter seem far more harsh than it actually is. The result is restlessness and dissatisfaction, and the dreamer gets out of life only a small fraction of the happiness and success of which he is capable.

Warning: You can't turn your back on reality and expect

those wish-fulfillment dreams to come true. Paradoxically, the only road to attainment of those dreams lies in *facing reality* and turning your back on fantasy. Fantasy is a robber. It dissipates one's energy, steals one's self-confidence.

• *Dreams Release Our Inhibitions*

The *second function* of the dream is the *release of inhibitions*. There are many things that we want or crave that we cannot get because society or our conscience in the waking state would not approve.

For example, William Jones is a married man, the father of several children, and a most respected member of his community. You would not suppose nor even imagine from his outward behavior that there was anything wrong with him. In point of fact, there is nothing wrong with him, but he is not happy in his home life.

The romance that led him to marry has long since worn off. The sweetheart that he knew long ago has now become a very prosaic wife. She does not cater to him as she used to, yet his heart still craves romance; he would like nothing better in this world than to have some woman make some fuss over him, telling him what a wonderful man he is.

But he is very prim, very austere, and very strict. He does not even dare to cast covetous glances on women, for that is wrong. But at night, when the censorship of consciousness is gone, all inhibition is removed and his mind is free to wander in any direction. He dreams himself in situations where not one woman but many are falling in love with him. He is lionized and adored as few men have ever been. For instance, he dreams how in a night club chorus girls flock to his table telling him how handsome he is and how envious they are of other women who adore him. They sit on his lap and smother him with kisses. And this pleases him a great deal because of the fact that his wife is so cold in actual marital relations. Because of this, his physical relations with his wife are very infrequent. But in the dream one woman after another makes love to him.

What is true of this man is probably true of his wife, who may be dreaming of a parallel situation. Life is funny!

Our *warning* to such a man and woman is to wake up to life's possibilities. It is much healthier and more deeply satisfying to find happiness and romance in real life than in dreams.

It is wise to check on those inhibitions responsible for such dreams. They are handicapping you physically as well as mentally; and to attain happiness, you must strive to overcome them. The man who never marries because he is too inhibited to propose, but who *dreams* he is happily married, is cheating himself. He allows himself only a pale *ghost-love* instead of the real emotion.

• *Dreams Release Accumulated Unhealthy Emotions*

A *third function* of dreams is to *release accumulated unhealthy emotions,* which society does not allow us to do during the day.

For instance, George Brown was bawled out by his boss, but poor Brown, although he felt very bitter about it, could not say a word to the boss for that might mean the loss of his job. Yet his feelings must find an outlet in some way; so at night he dreams that his boss was killed in an accident or that for some reason or another the boss was demoted and he, George Brown, was given the boss's place.

Hostility is a very powerful emotion of which society does not approve, but nobody can stop you from hating in a dream.

• *Dreams Hide Their Meanings in Symbols*

It must be pointed out that these dreams are not entirely unbridled. Our conscience, in some obscure way, exercises a control that we speak of as "censorship." When the wish-fulfillment is too crude and too obvious, the censorship disguises it in such a way that we are not even able to recognize it as such.

The dream then hides its meaning in *symbols* of various

kinds. This process of symbolization prevents us from being shocked too much by our unbridled emotions. George Brown really wanted to kill the boss, but his conscience would not permit him to be a murderer, not even in a dream. So the dream censor arranged to allow death to happen as though it were an accident.

Symbols in a dream also serve to camouflage the sexual content of the dream.

Warning: A series of so-called "bad dreams" in which we commit antisocial acts, signifies that we have criminal tendencies. It is necessary to be on guard against habitual destructive thinking, particularly if it is directed against certain individuals. Sooner or later, bitterness against society, hatred of those around us, unbridled sexual or criminal fantasies engender shame and self-hatred. These, in turn, cause emotional illness.

• *Dreams Take Us Back to Carefree Childhood*

A *fifth function* of the dream is *regression.* If life is not as pleasant as it might be, the dream provides us with a wonderful opportunity to relive that part of our life that is most pleasant to us. And is there in the life of any individual a part of life that was more pleasant than childhood? Then we did not have so many troubles and worries. We received affection from our parents and relatives. So it is not surprising when things do not move so smoothly during the day that at night we dream ourselves into early childhood. Let it not be supposed, however, that regression is characteristic only of neurotics. It is doubtful that there is a single human being who does not have occasional dreams of regression.

Here again is a word of *warning:* If you find yourself engaging in too many dreams of this kind, it probably indicates that you are retreating too much to the *past.* It will repay you far more to be concerned with the *present* and the *future.* The past is so much water over the dam. He cannot relive yesterday; what counts is what we do today, tomorrow, and the next tomorrow.

• Dream Life Is Sometimes Ambivalent

A *sixth function* is *bipolarity* (a term used by Stekel to describe opposing emotions such as *love* and *hate* existing at the same time.)

We learn that human beings are not always consistent in their feelings. Strange as it may seem, persons may entertain at the very same time, and with reference to the same situation, two opposite feelings: *love* and *hate*. Perhaps a good illustration is that of a woman who gives birth to an illegitimate child. Her maternal instinct prompts her to love the child and accept it as part of herself. The social situation, however, demands that she reject the child. Thus we have here a woman in whom acceptance and rejection vie with each other for supremacy, now one being on top, now the other. This reaction is also spoken of as *ambivalence,* another term for *bipolarity*. In people who cannot make up their minds in a particular situation it often leads to feelings of indecision.

For example, a young girl may confess her love for two suitors and, following a proposal from both, may be undecided as to whom to marry. She submits a number of dreams in which one of them is hurt or killed in an accident.

Thus we see that at the unconscious level she prefers one suitor to the other. Her dream-life serves to solve this conflict of indecision. The psychotherapist is able to eliminate the suitor toward whom the death wishes are directed, or toward whom she manifests the greatest amount of *bipolarity*.

• Dreams Can Repress Unhealthy Cravings

A *seventh function* is *repression*. It has already been mentioned that human beings in the particular social setting in which they live are not always able to satisfy all their cravings. Two avenues are left open to them: either to satisfy these cravings, regardless of social prohibitions, and thus become involved in criminal acts, or else to *repress* these cravings and remain good citizens at the expense of unsatisfied desires.

This is what the majority of people do. But desires are often very strange in their behavior and cannot be done away with entirely. Proscribed during the day, they emerge during the night in dreams in which they find a complete outlet. Yet, odd as it may seem, after the dream has satisfied all the desires completely, the conscience of the man does not feel quite at ease; he is *conscience-stricken* even though he has had only a dream. Hence the frequent *anxiety* with which the individual wakes up from such a dream.

A husband may have found it necessary to repress his anger directed against his wife in the waking state, but in dream-life he dreams that his wife died after a severe attack of pneumonia. He wakens feeling panicky and nervous as a consequence of the guilt feeling implied in the dream.

In the dream we sometimes find a repression of guilt. The tendency of the individual not to incur the disfavor of the society in which he lives is so great that it prevents him, even in dream-life, from being caught at committing some asocial act. Accordingly, in the enactment of the dream, instead of himself committing the crime he has somebody else commit it while he appears more as a witness and an onlooker to the whole thing. In this way the crime is committed, the wish is satisfied, but the dreamer cannot be held guilty.

• *Dreams Can Have Practical Value*

From the above it can be seen that if you make a careful study of quite a large number of your dreams and have learned how release of inhibition, repression, regression, bipolarity, and other mechanisms work as well as the role that emotions play in the unconscious, you will discover that dreams, instead of being mere caprice and expressions of superstitions and prejudice, have practical value when studied in a systematic way. The correct interpretation of one dream is sometimes verified by other dreams, because it is often found that the same trend remains in many dreams.

• *What about the Repeated Dream?*

A dream that keeps repeating itself over the years suggests a "root-conflict." Such a conflict can color your entire personality. A person who keeps dreaming of associating with famous people, of discovering the cure for insanity or cancer, or of acquiring great wealth is over-compensating for a deep-rooted inferiority complex.

There are people who dream constantly of falling. The repeated dream of falling may represent a temptation to go astray. It suggests yielding to your impulses. The impulse may be a sexual or even a suicidal one. Repeated dreams in which you find yourself in dangerous or frustrating situations suggest anxiety and fear. They may be the result of actual experiences in your past when life was threatened either by serious illness or an accident. Soldiers often experience "battle dreams" years after the war is over. These are also referred to as "echo dreams."

• How to Remember Your Dreams

You can train yourself to *recapture* your dreams. Try this interesting experiment. Go to bed with the intention of dreaming. As you fall asleep, let your mind wander. Have a piece of paper and a pencil handy on the bedside table. If in the middle of the night or early morning, you are awakened by your dream, turn on the light and jot it down. Then go back to sleep again.

If you are not awakened during the night, ask yourself before getting out of bed in the morning, "What did I dream about?" It is within those first five minutes of awakening that you are most apt to remember your dreams. If you fail the first few times, keep on trying. I can assure you that you will finally begin to recall them. Keep this up until you have collected a series of twenty-five to fifty written dreams. Read them over, study them carefully, and try to evaluate them in terms of what you are about to learn concerning the interpretation of your dreams.

• Interpreting Your Dreams

The first thing to know is that the dream is not a haphazard phenomenon, meaningless and senseless. However disconnected it may seem to you, it is part of the composite functioning of the mind.

There is no "hocus-pocus" to the interpretation of your own dreams. It is a fascinating task for logic and common sense. Treat each dream as if it were a piece of a jigsaw puzzle. When you have put together enough of the pieces, the picture will emerge. That picture may open your eyes to a new estimate of yourself. A new light on weakness in yourself that your conscious mind has been glossing over. A new light on a vague feeling of unhappiness or guilt haunting you.

"Know thyself!" In that knowledge lies your strength. Walk fearlessly and calmly into the world of your dreams and take stock of what you find there.

A Dream-Chart to Guide You

Common Dreams	Interpretation
1. Dreams of acquiring wealth.	Over-compensation for poverty or financial distress.
2. Dreams of romance.	Hunger for love.
3. Dreams of falling.	Fear of *yielding* to something disapproved by society or forbidden by your conscience.
4. Dreams of talking to a deceased relative.	The wish to deny the reality of their death or a desire to join them.
5. Dreams of being robbed.	Fear of financial insecurity.
6. Dreams of childhood (in old people).	Desire to be young again—a disguised fear of old age and approaching death.
7. Dreams of being attacked by wild animals (in women).	Fear of sexual seduction.
8. Dreams of being killed in an accident or dying of illness.	Feelings of guilt (a need for punishment, disguised suicidal wish).
9. Dreams of fire (getting burned).	Passion associated with a fear of temptation.
10. Dreams of close association with prominent people.	Over-compensation for feelings of social inferiority.

11. Dreams of darkness, of being buried alive, and of funerals.

Fear of death.

12. Dreams of indecision.

Lack of confidence and a fear of the future.

13. Dreams of success, achievement, and fame.

Inferiority complex.

14. Dreams of traveling.

A desire to run away from reality.

15. Dreams of always being late, of missing trains, busses, or appointments (in women).

Sexual frigidity.

16. Dreams of failure or bankruptcy (in middle-aged men).

Fear of sexual impotence.

17. Dreams of death of some living relative or friend.

Disguised death-wishes directed against that person.

18. Dreams of nakedness or semi-nudity in public.

Desire to release one's moral inhibitions.

19. Dreams of being threatened or finding oneself in a dangerous situation.

Fear of impending disaster.

20. Dreams of stealing, violating the law or assaulting someone.

Repressed criminal tendencies.

21. Dreams of hurting someone we love.

Feelings of ambivalence (love-hate attitude toward the same person).

22. Dreams of gaiety, celebrations, and fun-making.

Repressed unhappiness (a desire to escape from an unhappy environment).

23. Dreams of various sexual activities.

Wishful thinking (sexual repressions).

24. Dreams of being imprisoned, or struggling to escape.

Conflict (fear of being overcome by the hopelessness of one's frustrations).

25. Dreams of going insane.

Fear of doing something for which one is not *mentally responsible*.

• *Summarizing What We Have Learned about Dreams*

1. *Everyone* dreams; no one sleeps who does not breathe; neither does one sleep who does not dream. They are concomitant. There are those who recall their dreams and others who forget them. With training and persistence you can capture the dream before it vanishes.

2. The dream is the mirror of your *unconscious* thinking. It reflects the emotional conflicts you are suffering from at the unconscious level.

3. Your dreams serve to gratify the instinctual cravings that are repressed in the waking state. They have many functions, such as wish-fulfillment, release of inhibitions, release of accumulated unhealthy emotions, regression, and repression.

4. Physical conditions, such as hunger, pain, indigestion, and headaches, can influence the nature of your dream.

5. Dream-analysis will aid you in exposing the unconscious motivations behind your health-complaints.

6. If you are undergoing psychoanalysis, your dreams will serve to inform your analyst of the progress you are making and your attitude toward the treatment.

7. The purpose of dream-interpretation is to bring that which is repressed in the unconscious to a level of conscious understanding. The application of knowledge gained in this way should enable you to achieve a more satisfactory adjustment to life.

8. Keep a Dream Notebook. Record your dreams. When you have collected a sufficient number of them, begin to *study* them. Use what you have just learned about dream-analysis to guide you. There are books you can purchase dealing with dream-interpretation that will be of further help to you.[1]

---

[1] Wilhelm Stekel, *Interpretation of Dreams*, Vols. I and II. New York: Liveright Publishing Co., 1943 and Emil Gutheil, *The Language of the Dream*. New York: The Macmillan Co.

Session 4.

▄▗▄▀▄▗▄▗▄▗▄▄▗▄▗▄▗▄▗▄▗▄▄▗▄▗▄▗▄▗▄▗▄▄▗▄▗▄▗▄▗▄▗▄▄▗▄▗▄▗▄▗▄▗▄▄▗▄▗▄▗▄▀

Blaming Heredity
Doesn't Help

• *Facts and Fallacies about Heredity*

Fallacy: Nervous and mental disorders are *inherited*.

Fact: That one of your parents spent sometime in a mental institution is no indication that you are going to suffer a similar mental breakdown.

Many persons become *conscious* of what is often referred to as "tainted heredity" and use it as an *alibi* for their own shortcomings.

We are likely to inherit only a *predisposition* (tendency) to respond to specific situations with the same type of emotional reaction as our parents. I knew a family in which three of its members committed suicide. This might suggest that suicide is hereditary, but these individuals simply reacted to major frustrations in a similar way.

A patient once told me she was afraid to have children, because her mother-in-law had spent sometime in a mental institution. She was relieved when I assured her that insanity does not pass on from parents to children and quoted Dr. Karl Menninger:

> The scientific truth is that at the present time we
> have no convincing evidence that "insanity" or any

generally prevalent form of mental disease likely to result in insanity is definitely transmitted by heredity.

As to how we account for mental disorders being more prevalent in some families, the evidence indicates that patterns of similar reaction to similar frustrations among members of the same family are *imitated.* If a parent suffers from manic-depressive psychosis (a form of insanity) the son or daughter may react to an acute frustration the same way that the parent did, not because of any hereditary factor but because of sheer *suggestion* and *imitation.*

Fallacy: Personality traits and behavior defects are inherited.

Fact: Patterns of behavior-reaction and habits are *not* inherited. They are *acquired.* One does not inherit a compulsion to drink to excess, nervousness, hysterical recations, jealousy, temper tantrums, homosexual leanings, depressed moods, feelings of inferiority, or criminal impulses.

• *What Makes You What You Are?*

The nucleus of our personality is influenced by a *multiplicity* of factors. Dr. Karl Menninger lists them as follows:[1]

1. The teaching, training, and example of parents and the reactions to brothers and sisters.
2. Climate and weather.
3. The architecture of the home.
4. Food and fashions.
5. The influence of the school, church, newspapers, playmates, and society in general
6. Economic and social laws that modify behavior patterns.
7. The accidents of life, both physical and mental.
8. The illnesses, wounds, griefs, disappointments, and shocks of all kinds that come to everyone.

All these, Dr. Menninger maintains mold the personality.

This does not imply that *nothing* is inherited. It simply means that we cannot ascribe our weaknesses to heredity.

---

[1] Dr. Karl Menninger, *The Human Mind* (New York: Alfred A. Knopf, 1937), page 27.

• *See Yourself in 3 Dimensions*

Heredity → △ ← Environment

↑
Personality-Reaction

The term "heredity" suggests that we have no control over those elements that are found in our chromosomes. Heredity constitutes merely one side of the triangle. We are what we are today because of our *personal reaction* to *parental influences* and *environmental experiences*.

• *Our Personalities Must Adjust to Changing Situations*

In our struggle to survive, our personalities must of necessity adjust to changing situations from the time we are born.

It is this constant need to adjust to our environment—to handle each new situation wisely—that makes life complex and difficult for some people.

Whether we survive or perish depends on our personality-reactions to such unforeseen situations as ill health, disappointments, griefs, and financial reverses, among others.

• *Can You Ever Blame Your Parents?*

Neurotics like to make *neurotic* parents their *scapegoats.* It is an easy out. In Army parlance it amounts to "passing the buck." No one denies the fact that we are fortunate or unfortunate depending upon the emotional stability or instability of our forebears. It would be ideal if we could choose our four grandparents. They, like our parents, are wished upon us.

There is no doubt but that some parents are "delinquent" and lack the ability to bring up their children as mature, emotionally self-sustaining adults. They are often guilty of over-protection, over-nagging, or over-discipline. Too many of us have not been trained in childhood to expect disappointments, nor taught to react to them successfully. A good part of this responsibility falls upon our parents.

However, there is a tendency among many of us to assume a fatalistic attitude and hold our parents accountable for *everything*.

Dr. Jacob Conn in an article entitled "Don't Blame Your Parents"[2] relates how Sid Caesar, in the role of a psychiatris on a television program, was asked to diagnose a case of *insomnia*.

"Of course," he said, "We have to go back to what happened to the patient during infancy." After much thought he came to the conclusion that the patient's mother forgot to tell him to close his eyes.

Dr. Conn comments:

> Almost as ridiculous is the excuse offered by a woman I know for her unattractive appearance. When a friend asked her why she didn't wave her hair, powder her nose, or occasionally get an attractive new hat, she answered with a plaintive resignation: "When I was a child mother told me I wasn't good-looking!" It did not occur to her that as an adult it was up to her and nobody else to make the most of her looks.

He makes the final comment that "when a person continually focuses upon his unhappy childhood and the irreparable injury his parents did to him, you may be sure that there is more wrong with him than with his parents."

A young woman whose parents were divorced when she was a child confessed that she married only to get away from her neurotic parents. She told me that she had been unhappy most of her life, that she had never known what love meant. As a result she married the first boy she dated. Although the man she married was a good provider, kind and sympathetic, she constantly complained about being unhappy.

I tried to convince her that she too would end up in Reno seeking a divorce if she allowed herself to continue living in the unhappy past.

Such unhappy persons usually nurse feelings of self-hatred, which they project onto others.

---

[2] Dr. Jacob H. Conn, "Don't Blame Your Parents," *Reader's Digest,* October 1952, condensed from *Your Life.*

• Family-Slaves

A *family-slave* is a person who, being *emotionally immature*, has never been able to establish a healthy *detached* relationship to his parents—has never been able to think and act as an adult, to assume responsibility and become emotionally self-sustaining. The excessive attachment to or dependency on one or both parents is referred to by psychoanalysts as a *parent-fixation*. These fixations are generally brought about by a combination of factors. An over-solicitous mother may foster feelings of dependency in a son or daughter. Well-meaning parents often do harm by *spoiling* an only child.

• Emotionally Still a Child

To cite a brief example, a twenty-seven-year-old patient told me she developed the habit of chewing and swallowing toothpicks for the past two years. She explained it as a symptom of her restlessness and nervousness.

When she left the Midwest to come East to work, her mother demanded that she write a letter home every day. The contents of these letters between daughter and mother betrayed the extent of their neurotic attachment for each other. The patient suffered from symptoms of *adult-infantilism* (a term used by psychiatrists to describe persons with an infant-like dependency-complex).

Due to complications that ensued when she met a boy she cared for, she sought advice. I told her that she had never been psychologically weaned from her mother's breast, which accounted for the pleasure-habit of eating toothpicks. Because *she was emotionally still a child,* she was not mature enough for marriage. She gave up her habit, wrote to her mother at less frequent intervals, and began showing signs of becoming self-sustaining.

• The Child-Wife

A girl who has been spoiled by her parents may continue to be spoiled by a husband who feels sorry for her. Actually, she

wants to *remain a family-slave*. To grow up and develop
emotional maturity entails too much effort. She is plagued
with mental laziness.

When tragedy strikes, she goes all to pieces, has hysterics
or a "nervous breakdown." She makes a poor housekeeper,
careless, and untidy, and spends money unwisely. The children
get on her nerves. This all becomes complicated with feelings
of self-pity and lonesomeness.

Only recently a wife who classifies in this group came to the
office to confide that she was contemplating suicide. She pro-
ceeded to tell me what a fine husband she had, and how
unworthy she was of him; how, in fact, she lacked the qualifications of making a good wife for any man. She stated that
she never had to want for anything prior to marriage, never
had to dry a dish or dust a piece of furniture. She thought
everything of her parents and regretted having to leave home
when she married. She sobbed as she told me all this.

The wisdom of marriage for a wife who is a *family-slave*
lies in recognizing her true personality-portrait through *self-
analysis*. Once she has arrived at a *personality-diagnosis*, she
has a better chance to affect a cure for herself by changing her
behavior-attitude toward her husband.

The husband can cooperate in the meantime by neither
pampering his family-slave wife nor becoming indifferent or
abusive. He can offer helpful suggestions, keep himself under
control by subjugating his intolerance, and seek help and
advice if the marriage becomes too trying.

• *The Child-Husband*

The husband, who is himself a family-slave, is apt to be
suffering from a mother-fixation.

Dr. E. Strecker, made a special study of *Momism* (too much
mother-love) and showed that emotional immaturity is just as
common to the male sex. The mother who becomes a "mom,"
is unhappy in her marriage and diverts her possessive love to
her son. She plays up to him to win his complete devotion.
She becomes "the best mother in the world." The son's mar-

riage can be successful only if he marries a woman of his mother's type, and this often occurs if his wife is willing to accept a secondary role. His mother is the head of that family if she is still living. Even if she has gone or is living at a distance, his life and his reactions are tuned to her ideas. If his mother is dead, his wife has to assume the mother-role. He is one of her children, and she must treat him as the spoiled one—indulging his every wish, living her life unselfishly so that his happiness can be complete. She seldom succeeds in satisfying him because she cannot reach the ideal he has set up, *his mother*. Often there are no children in this family, for this husband denies all amorous feelings for his "mom" and therefore for his wife.

• *The Married Bachelor*

The married-bachelor is married only on paper. He goes through the formality of a ceremony, but it is a false marriage. Emotionally and psychologically he is still a bachelor and he remains one.

He doesn't marry with the idea of making himself a good husband or father. He marries with the idea of acquiring advantages for himself.

The *married-bachelor* has never been adequately prepared for life. Emotionally and sexually he is *immature*. He is motivated by an unconscious desire to re-establish a child-mother relationship. He looks for a wife who will be 90 per cent mother, not a companion with whom to share life. He is the boy grown up. He frequently marries because he is afraid society will think there is something wrong if he doesn't. More often, he marries as he would acquire a housekeeper. He contributes nothing but support. Emotionally, it is all intake and no output.

• *Yesterday's Handicap Can Be Tomorrow's Asset*

In looking over my records, I discovered that often a wife who was anxious to get a divorce came from divorced parents. The same holds true for husbands who blame their parents for the failure of their marriage.

It is more than a coincidence that persons who come from broken homes are more susceptible to marital unhappiness. Hence, it is important in taking stock of yourself to make sure that the unhappiness of your parents or the frustrations suffered in your early childhood do not unconsciously influence your present attitudes toward love, sex, and marriage.

Ask yourself these questions:

1. What was the nature of the relationship that existed between my mother and father?
2. Did my parents love each other?
3. If my parents divorced, what effect did a broken home have on me?
4. Did I come from a neurotic home environment? If so, what can I do about it?

In attempting to answer these questions, you may discover the source of your marital unhappiness; the neurotic influences that have carried over into your married life.

A patient who had left her husband following a quarrel ran back to her mother only to discover that she had been a victim of her mother's domination, that her mother (who had divorced her father) was highly neurotic and possessive. The patient realized how unhappy she was at home and returned to her husband. She planned in the future to analyze and discuss her grievances with her husband instead of her mother.

- *Neurotic Parents Are Victims of Their Own Unconscious*

One must remember that neurotic parents are *unconsciously* motivated. Their irritating acts are not deliberately thought out but are compulsive. They are literally compelled by pressures within to act as they do.

It accomplishes nothing to rail at your unfortunate heredity. Study and analyze your family-tree.

We all know of individuals who have made a success of their life despite the fact that as children they were exposed to all sorts of *traumatic experiences*. Having had parents who were *neurotic* need not be a life-long handicap.

• *It's Futile to Blame Your Parents*

A patient related how his father used to whip him, call him names, and predict that he would never amount to anything. Jim's mother was of the peasant type—subjugated to the iron will of a tyrannical husband. Instead of coming to her son's defense, she assumed a neutral role. Jim felt *rejected*. As he grew up he felt more *unloved* and *unwanted*. His sisters were favored and spared the abuse that the father meted out from time to time. All Jim remembers of his childhood is the constant bickering between his parents, the whippings he received from his father, and the economic insecurity that he felt as a result of having to work during his youth at a job he disliked intensely, instead of being given the opportunity to go to college.

• *Distorted Philosophy of Life*

The consequences of such a start in life were inevitable. Jim became "paranoid"—that is he became defensive, suspicious, felt he was living in a "dog-eat-dog" world. He became cynical and developed the distorted philosophy of life that everyone was out to get all he could at the expense of others. His tone of voice was belligerent. His facial muscles twitched. He never smiled. He talked fast, walked fast, could never relax, and whenever an opportunity presented itself gave full expression to his views about love, marriage, and the world in general.

Actually, this boy was *blaming his parents for all of his unhappiness.* He was afraid to trust people or to believe that there are men and women who are *unlike his parents.* Were he to marry with such an attitude toward life, he would no doubt treat his wife in the same way that his father treated his mother. That he was *a chip off the old block* was brought to his attention. He was made to realize that his ulcer of the stomach, which failed to respond to medication, was the price he paid for adopting a *man-against-himself* type of philosophy. He had formed a life-long habit of *blaming his heredity.* When he was told that he had made unhappiness a career he began challenging his carry-overs and brought about a remarkable change for the better in himself. He dissipated his hostility, began developing faith in himself and others, and finally showed signs of ultimately overcoming the unhappiness that he projected on to men and women whom he identified as father and mother-surrogates.

• *Follow These Eight Common Sense Rules*

Rule One: Don't use the incompatibility of your parents as an alibi for your own inadequacies. Holding resentment against your parents doesn't help. In "Your Key To Happiness" Harold Sherman states: "Whether you realize it or not, you are directly or indirectly responsible for everything that happens to you."

Rule Two: Make a list of your parents' personality-liabilities. Remind yourself not to *imitate* them. Neuroticism is contagious, not inherited.

Rule three: If you are a parent, or about to become one, give your children what you yourself may have been deprived of—a feeling of independence and emotional security.

Rule Four: Overcompensate for what you might consider a handicap by learning to be of some service to the world. Put purpose in your life.

Rule Five: Heed the advice of Douglas Lurton, author of "Make The Most Of Your Life": "Take the tools at hand and carve your own best life."

Rule Six: Don't bemoan the fact that you are not a Nobel Prize winner. Success is not always a matter of fame or fortune. You don't have to be brilliant to be normal.

Rule Seven: Stop behaving like a man-child, one who has never been able to detach himself from his mother's apron strings. When a man displays an excessive attachment to his family, particularly his mother, it should be a warning sign. It means marrying someone who will try to be half-husband and half-son and who will make a bad job of both.

Rule Eight: Stop being a child-woman, one who is extremely sensitive and possessive, requires a lot of attention, and is emotionally immature.

Rule Nine: Correct any erroneous conception you might have about "inherited traits." Stop rationalizing that you are a "chip off the old block," that you came from a "Bad Seed," that it must be in your blood and therefore you can't do anything about it. The kind of thinking you do today determines the kind of living you do tomorrow. So decide *today* the kind of a person you want to be *tomorrow. Stop blaming Fate.*

▄▀

Who Are Normal People?

● *What Constitutes Normality?*

According to Dr. Edward Glover of London, *normal* people are those who are free of symptoms, unhampered by mental conflicts, have a satisfactory work-capacity, and are able to love someone other than themselves.

The word "normal" is a relative term. What may be accepted behavior in one locality may be considered abnormal or socially offensive in another community. What may be a normal custom in Africa would be regarded as abnormal in New York.

The term therefore has an *elastic* meaning.

All of us are somewhat eccentric; we have our private quirks, pet superstitions, and fears. In this respect we are all alike.

● *All Human Beings Fit into One of Six Groups*

Actually one could classify the entire population of the world into six groups as follows:

1. The *normals*
2. The *neurotics*
3. The *psychotics* (the insane—over 500,000 in the the United States alone)

4. The *psychopaths* (criminals, hoboes, prostitutes, alcoholics, sex offenders, drug addicts, and so forth)
5. The *mental defectives* (the feeble-minded)
6. The *miscellaneous* (unclassified—including jungle inhabitants, natives, existing in remote parts of the world, and that part of the earth's population living 'en masse' in various countries who cannot fit into any classified group)

In an overall picture, the *normal* people of the world comprise merely one of six groups.

• *Personality Qualities of the Normal Person*

I have often been asked to describe *what makes a normal person normal*. It is because he is endowed with the following character traits—personality-assets that *you* too can develop.

1. He is emotionally mature; one not *fixated* (overly attached) to his parents; he thinks and behaves as a grown-up person and has a definite aim in life.
2. He accepts the hard knocks of life philosophically.
3. He keeps himself too busy to be unhappy.
4. He is able to earn his own livelihood and works without too much complaining.
5. He possesses a *joie de vivre*, a joy of living; he's glad to be alive.
6. He is able to get along with almost everyone, has a *flexible* personality, and is humanly understanding.
7. He does not act impulsively, has learned to control his emotions, exercises wise judgment, and is able to make intelligent decisions.
8. He is not a cynic, nor does he harbor neurotic prejudices.
9. He tries to keep his nose out of other people's affairs.
10. He is tactful and not argumentative, tolerant

and unselfish, not oversensitive, and able to accept criticism.
11. He has a sense of humor and radiates self-confidence.
12. He is capable of *giving* love, or sharing love with someone else, has faith in mankind, and possesses a healthy attitude toward people and the world around him.
13. He acquires wisdom through the experiences of past mistakes.
14. He has achieved a desirable way of life—one that makes living *pleasant* instead of *painful*. He has acquired an ability to *relax*—a capacity to *enjoy* life.

• *The Normal Husband*

The *ideal* husband is easily identified. Although he wears no medals, he is a hero in his own home. He is a hero in the sense that he is a very likable person, loved by his wife, respected and admired by men, idolized by children. He has a balanced personality and is capable of getting along with almost everyone. He says the right thing at the right time. He doesn't bully his wife nor make her feel he is dominating her; yet is dynamic and progressive, radiates a feeling of self-assurance, and is positive in his actions and free of neurotic indecision. He is demonstrative and generous with his lovemaking. Friends admire him for his poise, his worldliness, and broadmindedness.

There is no selfish motive behind his plans. He *gives* love rather than *expects* it. He is kind, considerate, and romantic. He is even-tempered; he discusses rather than argues controversial issues. He remembers to compliment his wife's cooking and praises her in the presence of others; he remembers birthdays and anniversaries. He is careful never to belittle her or appear too critical. He is not too proud to help with the dishes when circumstances require it.

He is sympathetic, yet firm to the extent of not pampering his wife. He knows the value of taking his wife out to

dinner occasionally or surprising her with a bouquet of
flowers. He makes home life enjoyable and makes his wife
feel she is the inspiration behind his success. He doesn't
object to doing odd jobs around the house and doesn't worry
needlessly. He proves that he can achieve a mutual and satisfying sexual adjustment. Moreover, he has a sense of humor
and can appreciate a woman's viewpoint.

You might stop me here and accuse me of describing a
myth of a man—one that doesn't exist. Not at all. This
type is not the "goody-goody" person who has no faults. He
is real and human and has a "psychopathic" taint to his
nature, devilish enough to make him fascinating. He loves
adventure and takes risks without being foolhardy. He can
enjoy an off-colored joke. He is neither a saint nor a sinner,
but believes in fair play. His disturbing tendencies are under
control. He may enjoy his liquor and have an eye for beauty,
but he prefers not to complicate his marriage either by alcoholic indulgence or by philandering.

The average man need not meet all these qualifications.
He needs only to attain 50 per cent of them to earn the badge
of being a well-integrated individual—a *normal* husband.

• *The Normal Wife*

A *normal* woman reminds herself that the average man
needs to have his ego inflated. She knows that every man
possesses an ego that may be likened to the skeletal structure
of his body. Without it he would be unable to stand erect
and walk. When this mental skeleton collapses, everything
suffers. A normal wife makes a man *want* to work, *want* to
succeed, and *want* to love. She encourages and inspires her
husband. This ego-inflation is the very thing a man finds in
the *other woman*.

A wise wife will be her husband's companion. She shares
his interests. She works with him and not against him. She
realizes that his future is her future. She grows with him
and manifests an appreciation of the better things in life.
She keeps herself detached from any unhappiness in her
family. She tries to forget the past and concentrates on the

present and the future. She realizes that excessive complaining is fatal to a happy marriage; that constant fussing, bickering, and nagging will only result in a chain of undesirable consequences—personality-incompatibility, sexual disharmony, divorce, and lonesomeness.

The normal wife cooperates rather than competes. She offers helpful suggestions rather than criticism. She knows how to advise her husband without making him feel that she wants to wear the pants.

She is sexually responsive, maintains a normal disposition, and does everything in her power to make her marriage a success.

• *Do Normal People Experience Frustrations?*

The answer is *yes.* No one is spared the sorrows of life. It is the *quality* and *quantity* of our individual nervous and mental reactions to each frustration that determines whether we are *normal* or *neurotic.* For example, everyone has spells of the blues. In most instances these emotional depressions ultimately disappear. We don't let them stand in the way of our normal activities.

When the neurotic is depressed he is ready to run up the white flag. He begins to feel sorry for himself and is incapacitated by his depression. The *healthy-minded* cautiously protect themselves against extremes in emotional reactions. They don't allow themselves to become over-elated or greatly depressed. They use constructive rationalization to avoid either extreme. When things go wrong they say to themselves: "It could be worse."

Normal people also worry and experience fears. But they keep them under control. They are able to distinguish between worries that are unfounded and those that are real. They do not become over-anxious, nor do they allow themselves to become paralyzed by neurotic anxieties.

• *How Do Normal People Think and Live?*

People who consider themselves well-adjusted exercise *moderation* in everything they do—eating, drinking, smoking, and so forth. They feed their minds with positive thoughts. They are able to make wise decisions and stick by them. They take adversities in their natural stride and manifest evidence of *emotional maturity*. Someone once asked Freud what a person had to do before he could be considered *mature*. Freud's reply was simple and brief. *"Lieben und arbeiten"* (one must be able to *love* and to *work*).

The best description of "maturity" I have ever encountered is one by Dr. Edward A. Strecker in his book *Basic Psychiatry* (Random House, N. Y., 1942).

> Maturity is a quality of personality made up of a number of elements. It is stick-to-itiveness, the ability to stick to a job, to work on it, and to struggle through until it is finished, or until one has given all one has in the endeavor. It is the quality or capacity of giving more than is asked or required in a given situation. It is this characteristic that enables others to count on one; thus it is reliability. Persistence is an aspect of maturity; persistence to carry out a goal in the face of difficulties. Endurance enters into the concept of maturity; the endurance of difficulties, unpleasantness, discomfort, frustration, hardship. The ability to size things up, make one's own decisions, is a characteristic of maturity. This implies a considerable amount of independence. A mature person is not dependent unless ill. Maturity includes a determination, a will to succeed and achieve, a will to life. Of course, maturity represents the capacity to co-operate; to work with others, to work in an organization and under authority. The mature person is flexible, can defer to time, persons, circumstances. He can show tolerance, he can be patient, and, above all, he has the qualities of adaptability and compromise. Basically, maturity represents a wholesome amalgamation of two things: 1. Dissatisfaction with the *status quo*, which calls forth aggressive, constructive effort, and 2. Social concern and devotion. Emotional maturity is the morale of the individual.

Normal people keep in close contact with things that stimulate and inspire them, such as beautiful music, art, literature, love, and religion. They cultivate sound living habits, develop a healthier way of thinking and living compatible with peace of mind. They know what they want and follow well-formulated plans for achieving their goals in life. They may not be entirely happy, but one thing is certain—they refuse to allow themselves to be defeated by any unkindness of Fate. They realize that life is short and that *living in the past is wasted energy;* consequently they live for *today* and *tomorrow.*

Session 6.

~~~~~~

To Be "Neurotic" Is not Always a "Handicap"

• *What Is a Neurosis?*

The word "neurotic" as used today generally has a derogatory implication. Few understand the true meaning of this term they use so glibly.

Recently, a woman friend of mine asked me: "Just who is a *neurotic?*"

I informed my friend that we are *all* a bit neurotic. Some of us are *normally* neurotic or to use a better phrase "not too neurotic." Others are neurotic in the sense that they are incapacitated by their neurosis. "Neurosis" means an *exaggerated* reaction of the mind and nervous system to health-ailments or unpleasant experiences.

The lack of understanding about the psychology of neurotic illness makes people unsympathetic and intolerant of neurotics.

A neurosis in other words, is an illness caused by unconscious motives, generally advantageous to the neurotic. The symptoms are trying to express (what psychiatrists call "body-language") and finding the purpose the particular symptom serves.

● *Common Types of Neuroses*

There are various kinds of neuroses (the word "psychoneurosis" that we hear so much of today means the same as "neurosis"). The following are a few of the more common types:

1. *Neurasthenia.* Fatigue is the predominating symptom, although the neurasthenic may also complain of vague aches and pains.
2. *Hysteria.* Emotional instability is the most characteristic symptom. The mental conflicts express themselves through symptoms that affect various parts of the body. For example, a wife who is unhappily married may complain to her husband about her "backaches." Psychiatrists use the term "conversion symptoms" because it actually describes what happens—the unhappiness or mental conflict is *converted* into an actual physical symptom.
3. *Hypochondriasis.* You have often heard someone referred to as a "hypochondriac." This means that there is always something ailing him, usually something imagined. He is overconcerned about his health and enjoys talking about his many ailments. I once asked a woman patient to tell me what she complained of. When she finished the recital, I had a list of 57 different symptoms. These people become "professional" patients going from doctor to doctor for relief.
4. *Anxiety.* Worry and fear are capable of causing a number of disturbances in many individuals. A neurosis of this type produces a chronic state of tension. In this group we find those persons who are victimized by all sorts of anxiety fears, (fears of elevators, crowds, germs, sex, insanity, death, and many others). Their feeling of insecurity keeps them on edge. They never relax. They are in a constant state of nervous exhaustion.

Whatever the particular neurosis may be, the psychology of its development is practically the same. Fear-thinking neurotics are victims of unconscious motivations. In any event neuroses are *curable.*

• The Neurotic Personality

Neurotics are chronic worriers, individuals who are excessively sensitive, over-aggressive, extremely shy, or easily depressed, who indulge in *negative* thinking and are inclined to be tense and nervous with or without provocation. They do not react well to personal frustrations. They are inclined to be *dreamers* rather than *doers.* As Claude Bristol put it: they have a *wishbone* but no *backbone.* However, if you probe into their inner personality you'll find that basically they are *nice* people.

The neurotic who is self-centered and self-conscious needs to be made *unself-conscious.* Nothing so mitigates against his recovery so much as humiliating him by making him feel responsible for his illness. Too many relatives make the mistake of classifying the neurotic in the same category as a *malingerer* —one who feigns illness.

• Neurotics Are not Always Failures

With insight and proper cooperation the neurotic need not go through life *handicapped.* Once he understands the psychology of his neurotic personality he can convert his neurosis into a blessing in disguise. You don't have to be *glad* you're neurotic. Neither do you have to be *sad.*

Many famous figures in history who rose above the herd, were *neurotic*—scientists, musicians, artists, writers. They were neurotic in the sense that they were temperamental and sensitive and occasionally lost control of their emotions.

We all have friends who are neurotic. Many of them are very talented and capable of making worthwhile contributions to life. To get along with them you must make an attempt to understand them.

• Neurotics Often Mean Well

The hostility that many neurotics display and project on to

others is superficial. If they cry easily and complain frequently it is only because they wish to attract attention, to be made to feel *secure* and *accepted*. They are children at heart, starved for affection and understanding.

Roberta, the mother of a two-year old child had seen a disturbing movie at one of the local theatres and became panicky, thinking that she too would go insane. She had identified herself with the character in the picture.

Fears of something happening to one's state of mind are common. They are referred to by psychiatrists as *"obsessive-compulsion neuroses."* When Roberta repeatedly complained of the fear of losing her mind, her husband, Tom, became intolerant, ridiculed her, and even threatened to leave her unless she "snapped out of it." Tom, like most other husbands, faced with a similar situation said; "I can't understand my wife. She's just not the same person. All she thinks about is this fear of going insane. I get so disgusted at times, I feel like walking out on her. I can't put up with it much longer. I admit I've gotten mad recently, thinking what she needed was some good rough talking to, but it didn't work. I'm at the end of my rope. I don't know what to do."

His attitude is typical of a husband or some other relative toward anyone who suffers from fears, indecision, or depression, or complains of numerous health-ailments. Tom had to be re-educated. He was instructed not to pamper his wife, nor should he scold or abuse her. He had to learn to develop the kind of attitude that a nurse or doctor takes toward a patient who is suffering from a physical illness.

In truth, Roberta was a devoted wife and a good mother, but she had become frightened and as a result incurred the neurotic illness called "obsessive-compulsion neurosis." She began to feel sorry for herself and kept repeating: "I don't blame my husband. I know I am making him very unhappy. I don't want to be this way, but I can't help it. I just don't have any confidence in myself. I'm always thinking of something happening to me."

As I said before, a feeling of *insecurity* is common to most neurotics. They wish to be assured that nothing disastrous

will happen to them. But assurance alone will not always eliminate their fear because they interpret it as false encouragement. Sometimes only a psychiatrist is able to explain the
unconscious factors behind their devastating fears.

• How to Manage a Neurotic

To handle a neurotic at home or at work, one fundamental
principle must be kept in mind. You must feel convinced that
neurotics are not to be despised. *Intolerance* is fatal to the
cure of the neurotic. If you penetrate the outer personality
of the average neurotic you'll discover that within he is sincere
and at heart a nice person. *Use the positive approach.* Bring
to his attention his *potentialities.* The results are surprising.
Most relatives use the negative approach, reminding them of
their inadequacies.

• Be Firm but Kind

On the other hand, using a stereotype pep-talk or flattery
only makes matters worse. *Firmness* and *kindly understanding* are the key methods of successfully helping those whose
entire thinking has turned inward to themselves. Get them
interested in doing things that bring them satisfaction. Neurotics want people to show an interest in them, to like them
whatever their shortcomings. They need friends who can
help them to live more satisfyingly. Remember a person who
is neurotic is no more to blame for his condition than a person
who has contracted a physical affliction.

• Intolerance Makes Matters Worse

Psychiatrists often succeed when others fail only because
they act as a *parent-substitute.* They listen, explain, and
advise and become the patient's personal manager. This bene-
ficial emotional relationship between patient and doctor is
called "transference." Oftentimes the patient gets well because the psychiatrist makes him feel that he is really a *nice*
person, whatever others have led him to believe. It is unintelligent to dislike sick people.

Occasionally, one hears someone say: "If a certain individual is difficult to get along with I try to make it my business to become his friend. I soon discover that he is a much nicer person than most people think."

As previously stated, neurotics behave as they do only because they are driven by unconscious motives. Actually, there are no down-in-the-heart mean people in this world. Abnormal behavior, whether neurotic, criminal, or psychotic, is the result of a sickness of the mind in one form or another. Dr. Ben Karpman, a well known psychoanalyst who is famous for his studies of the criminal, has found a *basic goodness* in many of those who break the law and has discovered that their crimes represented a symptom of an inner unhappiness that is traceable to childhood.

• The Law of Overcompensation

According to Dr. William James, an eminent Harvard Professor of philosophy, many of us (more especially neurotics) do not make the most of what we already have. Dr. James tells us:

> Compared to what we ought to be we are only half awake. We are making use of only a small part of our physical and mental resources. Stating the thing broadly the human individual thus lives far within his limits. He possesses powers of various sorts which he habitually fails to use.[1]

Being neurotic can be an *asset*—often it gives you a drive that results in your getting more out of life than you ordinarily would have, had you not been so handicapped.

When a kidney has been removed, the other kidney does the work of two. This is the law of overcompensation, which comes to our rescue whenever Fate challenges our will to survive.

• Feeling Sorry for Yourself Only Makes You More Neurotic

There can be little sympathy for the neurotic person who stews in his own self-pity and refuses to do anything about his liabilities.

---

[1] Dr. William James, *Letters of William James,* Volume 2, 1906 edition.

In a letter, a young woman of 31, wrote:

> When I was four I had scarlet fever. It left my eyes crossed, and I had to wear glasses. If a boy friend called for a date, half the time I would refuse, and if I accepted I would break the engagement at the last minute. I was very sensitive and developed an inferiority-complex. I used to feel sorry for myself. Recently, I had my eyes operated on and the operation was a success. My confidence is restored. I feel proud that I finally did something about my eyes rather then continue feeling sorry for myself.

• *The Girl Who Refused to Grow Up*

In another instance, I was driving out to see a patient, who, her family assured me, was in too shattered condition to come to my office. On the way, I picked up a young soldier, who was on his way to a local Army hospital. I noticed that his right arm had been amputated.

He was cheerful, talkative, and ready for a laugh. I avoided any mention of his empty sleeve and finally he said, "I'm surprised you don't ask me where I lost my arm. Most people want to know where I fought, how I lost it, and all the details."

"Isn't that pretty painful for you?" I wanted to know.

"Well . . . it was. But I can take it now. I know what to expect from people, so I don't shrink from it. I made up my mind to 'conk' the neurotic self-pity, no matter what. I knew if I didn't make my mind behave, I'd be sunk."

He paused, looked out into the darkness. "Sometimes at night my mind used to go wild. I'd be in a cold sweat." He broke off abruptly, and his voice strengthened. "I've got my self-pity right where I want it now. I've made up my mind to enjoy life. After all, I can see . . . I can hear . . . I can walk . . . and work."

When I left him he stood at the hospital gate, waved his one arm and said, "Thanks for the lift, Doc." It was the other way around, I thought . . . I got the lift.

The patient I had to see that day turned out to be a young girl who was having *hysterics* because her parents had refused to buy her a new convertible. On my return home, I could not help compare the soldier who refused to feel handicapped with the girl who refused to mature.

• Never too Late for Love

The other day I received a letter from a 72-year-old widower. He had read an article of mine and wanted to know if he was being *neurotic* in wanting to marry a 65-year-old widow with whom he had much in common. It pleased me to have the opportunity to congratulate him upon his "never-too-old-for-love" attitude and send my blessings for a happy wedding.

• Life Is What You Make It

If your life for one reason or another has been *loveless,* you can overcompensate by finding substitute pleasure in your work, in a hobby, or in a civic project. The joy of accomplishment can bring you peace of mind. There are enough good things in this world to make life enjoyable. Life *can* be beautiful.

$\mathcal{S}$ession 7.

‾‾‾

Your Ailments May Be Psychosomatic

• *The Influence of the Mind on the Body*

What affects the mind affects the body, and vice versa.

The word "psychosomatic," a relatively new term for many, is derived from the Greek "psyche" meaning *soul,* and "soma" meaning *body. Psychosomatic medicine* recognizes the powerful effect of the mind on the body's health and functioning.

There was a time when only the *physical* aspects of an illness were considered important in diagnosis. A patient who complained of stomach pains was examined, x-rayed, given medication or diet, or recommended for surgery.

• *The Greeks and the Romans Knew about Psychosomatic Sickness*

The science of medicine was not entirely blind to the emotional element in illness. As far back as the early Greek physicians, it was recognized that any disturbance of the soul affected the body as well. The Romans were also aware that the mind and the body were inseparable as evidence by their adage *Mens sana in corpore sano* (A sound mind in a sound body. While we have long accepted the fact that emotion could affect us physically, it has only been recently that we have realized the *extent* of the effect.

● *Emotional Conflicts Can Cause a Variety of Illnesses*

Today doctors know that habitual anger can produce stomach ulcers and marked elevations in blood pressure. Dr. Alvarez of the Mayo Clinic, who has had wide experience with the treatment of various digestive disorders, found that in many instances an *emotional disturbance* aggravated the physical illness. Physical disorders of all kinds have been found to be so closely linked with emotions that in many of the leading medical centers of the country doctors generally investigate the emotional factors before making a final diagnosis.

● *The Language of Psychosomatic Symptoms*

Dr. Frank G. Slaughter in his book *Your Body and Your Mind* [1] makes this significant statement: "We strive to be healthy in order to be happy, but how many of us strive to be happy in order to be healthy?"

Many people manifest unhappiness through the language of physical symptoms. Some develop hives or other nervous skin conditions; others perspire to excess, particularly in the palms of their hands; there are those who suffer from asthma brought on by mental causes; many complain of frequency of urination (nervous bladder). Tension in certain individuals results in migraine-like headaches, while vomiting, loss of appetite, diarrhea, gas pains, and heart-burn may indicate a reaction to an unpleasant life-situation.

The person who complains of nervous headaches and dizziness may be trying to accomplish too much at work, assuming too many responsibilities, and worrying about the consequences of his decisions. His dizziness represents his attitude toward a bad state of business affairs (everything going round and round). Another individual may develop a severe headache when he tries to figure out his income tax, but finds it

---

[1] Dr. Frank G. Slaughter, *Your Body and Your Mind*. New York: New American Library of World Literature.

a pleasure to calculate the profits of a good business transaction.

• A Case of Headaches Caused by Sexual Frustration

A patient, aged 30, married, the father of two children, complained that he was very unhappy in his married life. His wife was sexually frigid with the result that he never had satisfactory sexual relations. In addition to other symptoms such as dizziness, loss of weight, and vague aches and pains, he complained of *persistent headaches*. He separated from his wife. This afforded him some relief. The wife consulted me at his request, and they decided to give the marriage another chance. As soon as their sexual relations improved, the husband no longer experienced his headaches.

• Symptoms Have Symbolic Meanings

Psychiatrists today are unraveling many of the mysteries surrounding illnesses and symptoms that fail to respond to medication. Diarrhea may be correlated with emotional instability (lack of control). Constipation sometimes exists in a person who fears economic insecurity (a hoarding complex). Excessive sweating is often the consequence of fear. Pains around the heart (those not due to any heart disease) may be an expression of guilt (with a fear of dropping dead). A lack of appetite (*anorexia nervosa*) may be symbolic of a wish to die (suicidal tendencies: no food—no life). Multiple aches and pains can be disguised expressions of chronic unhappiness. Painful menstruation (*dysmenorrhea*) has often been associated with painful sexual intercourse (*dyspareunia*) common to women who subconsciously do not wish to accept the role of a woman during intimate relations.

• Mental Discord Is a Common Cause of Psychosomatic Disturbances

The following case involved marital incompatibility between a wife who suffered from painful menstrual periods and a husband who constantly complained of "feeling tired." These symptoms manifested themselves shortly after they married, at which time they became aware of their sexual discord.

At the time the husband was courting his wife, she had been going with a rival suitor. She claimed she loved this other person and considered him the more eligible candidate for marriage. The husband however, succeeded in persuading his wife to make the decision in his favor. On the honeymoon night she began to cry and began thinking of the other person (ghost love; psychic infidelity). She humiliated her husband and went so far as to confess that she had been intimate with her former lover, and that his technique of lovemaking was superior. The husband, upon learning of this, became *impotent*. Things went from bad to worse. They quarreled over trifles until it led to a threatened separation.

The wife was what psychoanalysts refer to as a "masculine protest" type, dominating, over-aggressive, and extremely career-minded.

She did not know that she had "psychically castrated" her husband by confessing her premarital intimacies. The husband on the other hand, was weak, passive, and infantile. He idealized women and was greatly inhibited and inexperienced. However, there was a sadistic component at work in his impotence, for he unconsciously gained revenge-satisfaction by frustrating his wife.

Psychoanalysis of both husband and wife revealed the emotional causes of their *psychosomatic* complaints. Their relationship improved to a point where they decided to remain together. Their marriage had been definitely a *competitive* one, both emotionally and sexually. The painful menstrual cramps diminished until they disappeared completely, and the husband restored his potency and no longer complained of chronic fatigue.

Thus we see that sexual conflicts are capable of disturbing the function of various organs of the body producing *psychosomatic* ailments of various kinds.

● Illness Caused by Sex Guilt

I recall another patient who actually became *nauseated* at the thought of having to discuss her sex life in the course of being psychoanalyzed. She had been suffering from a facial tic, (muscle twitch on the right side of her face). She was unmarried and claimed that the subject of sex was repulsive to her. She finally confessed that she had been resorting to self-gratification and the guilt feelings associated with it caused her to take on this defensive attitude of disgust as a means of avoiding the subject and thereby camouflaging her sexual practice. Her tic disappeared when she accepted the fact that it represented an unconscious expression of her sense of guilt.

● A Case of Emotionally-Induced Eye Disturbance

Another patient, aged 47, wearing bifocal glasses, came to the office complaining of feeling "jittery and nervous." During the interview he had a tendency to close his eyes so that he could barely see out of them. His chief complaint was as follows: "My eyes bother me. I can't read continuously. When I read it affects my throat and larynx. The muscles of my eyes tighten up. I can't do my work with my eyes like they are. There must be something wrong with the nerves of my eyes."

This patient told how he and his wife were constantly bickering and quarreling. When the incompatibility was corrected the eye symptoms disappeared.

● Understanding the Language of the Unconscious

The kind of psychosomatic ailment a patient develops quite often depends on the nature of the particular conflict. The symptom, when translated into the language of the unconscious, generally yields the *cause* of the neurosis. Many people express dissatisfaction with something *intolerable* via a stomach disorder (vomiting, loss of appetite, ulcers) or some other digestive disturbance (diarrhea, colitis, constipation).

• *Mental Indigestion*

The interrelationship between the digestive tract and the mind has been known to doctors since the time of Hippocrates in the year 640 B. C. However, only recently have specialists of gastro-intestinal disorders become aware of the extent of this influence of the emotions on one's alimentary tract.

It has been clinically demonstrated that emotional frustrations are capable of affecting the flow of hydrochloric acid in our stomachs. Many men who have never learned to relax, who are tense, nervous, and over-ambitious are susceptible to the development of ulcers. Certain types of occupations tend to make some individuals more prone to ulcer development. Builders and business executives very often develop an "ulcer personality." Ulcers are not uncommon among surgeons. Anyone who works under excess tension and pressure is a potential candidate. Incidentally, ulcers are not restricted to the male sex as is commonly believed. There are just as many women who become victims of ulcered stomachs.

• *The Ulcer Personality*

Dr. Flanders Dunbar, author of *Mind and Body* and a leading authority in the field of psychosomatic medicine contributes some interesting insights into the psychological make-up of the *ulcer personality.* She tells us that:

> The ulcer patient in his childhood usually is devoted to his mother, and yet he cannot be satisfied with the dependence which that devotion implies. As he grows older, he is continually torn between his impulse to lean on his mother, wife, friend, or employer and his compulsion to assert his own independence. It is his desire to escape from his own fear of being a clinging vine, which causes him to reach out for responsibility and gives him the appearance of the go-getter and often causes him to climb quite high in the ladder of worldly success.
>
> There is not in this personality the drive to excel which characterizes others, the coronary type, for example. The ulcer patient's ambition and activity

are merely a cloak for his dependent pull. He wants only to be active and escape from his own suspicion of inferiority; he does not necessarily seek to rival others, to climb over them, to impress his superior abilities upon them.

The early upsets connected with eating are the same factors which ultimately bring on ulcers. In order to overcome his hidden wish to be mothered, the ulcer patient will exaggerate his ambitions and self-assertive traits to the point of appearing positively aggressive. He refuses help; he reaches out for new responsibilities; he assumes unnecessary burdens. Insofar as these qualities make for success in business or professional life, the typical ulcer personality is an asset in propelling its owner to the top of the ladder. But the individual himself is just as likely to get the same satisfaction out of excessive work and emotional drive in the operation of a truck as in the conduct of a vast interlocking empire of industry.[2]

She concludes that many of these ulcer patients who are assertively independent individuals can be helped to understand themselves. Their cure can be permanent with proper medical treatment and *psychotherapy*.

• *The Unhappiness Settled in His Stomach*

An acquaintance who thought he was developing an ulcer invited me to dinner, a perfect meal prepared by his wife. When I complimented my hostess, her husband remarked: "I know I'm fortunate in having married such an excellent cook. But it seems that I can't appreciate good food. About an hour after I finish eating I begin to suffer from indigestion, cramps in the pit of my stomach, nausea, gas, and heartburn."

I became curious and asked if he had recently undergone a thorough physical examination. He replied, "Doc, they gave me the works. They x-rayed my entire digestive tract, looked at my stomach through a fluoroscope, and passed some kind of a rubber tube down my food pipe for what reason I don't know. All this was done at the diagnostic clinic of the medical center. The doctor finally concluded that since they found nothing physically wrong with me. that I must be suffering

---

[2] Dr. Flanders Dunbar, *Mind and Body*. New York: Random House, 1947.

from nervous indigestion. It seems that no matter what medicine I take or what I eat, I never get permanent relief."

Not wanting to devote the evening's conversation to his complaint, I suggested that he come to my office the following morning. Much to my surprise, I discovered the next day that he was unhappy in his marriage. His wife was an extreme introvert, did not mix well, and had a tendency to bring up unpleasant discussions at dinner. For example, she repeatedly reminded him of the bills they owed and the possibility of losing their home because they might not be able to meet the payments.

Upon hearing all of this, I arranged for an interview with his wife. At this time I gave her specific instructions never to discuss finances or anything unpleasant at mealtime. She cooperated well and made a sincere effort to refrain from unnecessary bickering, to display a more cheerful disposition, to invite congenial friends occasionally to dinner, and to become more demonstrative in her affection for her husband.

The results were astounding. Within a month my friend began telling me of the change he noticed in his appetite. He was no longer afraid to eat the things that previously had given him so much distress and was now willing to accept the original contention that his indigestion was intimately associated with his emotional relationship to his wife. I have corresponded with this couple for the past 11 years, and it is a source of gratification to learn that the husband has never had any more trouble with his stomach.

• Guilt Feelings Can Cause Ulcers

Another patient, a professional man, aged 26, single, was referred to me for psychoanalytic treatment because of a stomach complaint. He suspected that his duodenal ulcer was the result of *feelings of guilt* associated with certain sexual transgressions in his past. This insight he had acquired from reading magazine articles pertaining to psychosomatic disorders. He worried about having permanently damaged himself, and as a result developed a severe case of anxiety-neurosis.

His life-history disclosed that he had had stomach trouble since early adolescence. At the age of 14, one day at school, he felt nauseated, experienced pain in his stomach, and fainted. From then on he had recurrent stomach aches. At the age of 17 he was told that he had a duodenal ulcer and was placed on a milk diet. He had been rejected from military service because of his stomach trouble.

During analysis he admitted that he had a fear of driving an automobile, of thunder and lightning, and of being unhappy all his life. He concluded that he would never get over his feeling of guilt and consequently would always have stomach pains.

There existed a family predisposition toward stomach disorders. His parentage was definitely neurotic in character, and this undoubtedly exerted a traumatic influence on his emotional development. His sexual activities produced strong feelings of guilt. The nausea and vomiting represented a psychosomatic expression of his attempt to reject his sexual neurosis. Unable to repress his feelings of guilt, he developed an ulcer.

Following the completion of his analysis he made a satisfactory heterosexual adjustment, married, and became the father of a child. His ulcer healed, and he has had no recurrence of any gastro-intestinal distress. He reported that he was making a good economic and social adjustment and had resolved the guilt-complex that had caused the anxiety responsible for his ulcer.

• *When the Mind and the Stomach Are Married to Each Other*

Thus we see that the process of digestion has its *mental* as well as its *physical* aspects. In the life of everyone, there occurs situations that are agreeable or disagreeable, capable of influencing our stomach and intestines. You have often heard such common expressions as: "He makes me sick to my stomach"; "He has no guts"; "I was so scared, I had diarrhea"; "The thought of it alone makes me vomit." The stomach has been regarded by some as the *seat of emotions*.

A wife's nausea may signify her way of saying her husband's behavior makes her sick to her stomach. We know, too, that many women who find themselves with an unwanted pregnancy are prone to frequent vomiting (the stomach tries to reject that which the mind does not wish to accept.)

Many and many a case of supposed "indigestion" has its foundation in worry or undue anxiety. Mr. Williams is scheduled to deliver an important speech. He is nervously "on edge." At the banquet table, he is served some rich and exotic foods. He partakes: suffers "indigestion," and of course blames the food, which had little or nothing to do with his upset. Thereafter whenever Mr. Williams meets this particular concoction he suffers a fear reaction. He worries about it, anticipates, and not infrequently encounters trouble.

We have ample evidence to prove that among many neurotics *the mind and the stomach are wedded to each other*. One investigator discovered that an important emotional problem existed in two-thirds of the patients who presented themselves at a clinic devoted to digestive disorders. Wilber and Millis studied the records of 354 patients who, after examination at the Mayo Clinic, received a diagnosis of "nervous indigestion," and who were reexamined at the clinic more than seven years later. In 303 cases no evidence of organic disease was found in the follow-up examinations.

• The Price of Being Oversensitive

It is more than a coincidence that people who are very *sensitive* have a *sensitive stomach*. Dr. Austin Fox Riggs discovered that children who were oversensitive were not only overprone to weep, but also suffered from disturbances of digestion. "They may lose their appetites, their bowels may become disturbed, or they may even react emotionally to painful situations by an attack of vomiting."

A patient related how her seven year old daughter would vomit at will whenever her mother left her in the care of the maid. The vomiting was symbolic of her sense of insecurity. In another instance, a young boy complained of being car-

sick and would regurgitate his food whenever his parents took
him for a long trip. It was revealed that his brother was favored by the father. The boy overcompensated for his frustration by gaining greater attention from his father through
sickness. When the situation was corrected and it was explained to the boy that he was oversensitive and should not
be jealous of his older brother, the symptoms disappeared completely.

• *Unconscious Motivations Behind Psychosomatic Ailments*

Behind psychosomatic ailments lie definite motives. Cutting weeds only improves their growth. They must be pulled
up by their roots. And so with psychosomatic complaints,
the unconscious meaning of the symptoms must be uprooted
and brought to the surface of conscious understanding.

Psychoanalysts have discovered the various motives responsible for emotionally-induced ailments.

• *The Guilt Motive*

Many persons harbor exaggerated feelings of built because
of their super-sensitive conscience. That which they feel
guilty about they want to conceal from their family or friends.
They have a need for *self-punishment*. The following illustra-
tions are examples of this tendency.

Recently a patient whose wife had left him because of his
philandering activities consulted me regarding his heart pains.
"I've been told by a heart specialist that there is nothing
wrong organically with my heart," he said. "Yet, I'm not
convinced. In fact I think any moment I may succumb to
a fatal heart attack."

Since his wife's departure, he had engaged in numerous
affairs with women and acknowledged that he was an unworthy husband and an undeserving father of his four-year-
old child. Briefly, his symptoms represented his way of punishing himself for the guilt he felt following his infidelity. I
explained to him, "You remind me of the man who abuses
his stomach by over-indulging himself, takes his bicarbonate

of soda for relief, and repeats his over-eating the next day. Don't you see, you are playing a game, using my office as a 'confessional' for your guilty feelings. As long as you are willing to pay the price of feeling miserable—your way of bribing your conscience with neurotic suffering—you feel justified in continuing your pleasure-seeking activities. But this only adds to your original guilt. As soon as you give up your harem of women friends your mind and heart will be reconciled."

There are innumerable examples of persons who unconsciously are "knocking themselves out" because of their need for self-punishment following some transgression. Most of them are unaware that the symptoms of which they complain represent an attempt to punish themselves for their wrongdoings.

• *Guilt-Cancer*

A woman, age 28, developed severe headaches about a month prior to her husband's return from overseas duty. She was obsessed with the idea that she was developing a cancer of the brain. Like an escaped criminal who is finally captured, the hidden clue behind her migraine-like headaches came to light. About the time she first began to suffer these thumping sensations in her head, she had committed adultery. What she was suffering from was a *cancer of her conscience*. When she was told that the guilt was eating at her mind, she arrived at the conclusion that becoming a neurotic invalid was a poor way of apologizing for what she had done. I told her also that it was bad enough to feel guilty without making herself sick because of it. She felt that she had relieved her conscience by telling me about it and decided to give her husband the kind of welcome he deserved, minus the self-induced headaches.

• *The Erotic Motive*

It was some time before I began to appreciate the fact that some people actually get a kick out of their fears.

An unmarried woman, aged 42, informed me that she be-

came nervous and upset if she heard anything unpleasant—
such as someone being very ill. The thought of anyone dying
frightened her. If by chance she saw a funeral passing or
someone hurt in an accident she would be sick at her stomach
for the rest of the day. Yet this same woman would go to
the movies to see pictures like "Frankenstein"; would read
detective stories about murders, and was the first to run to
the scene of an accident. What else could one conclude? Her
fears became an erotic substitute for desires that she couldn't
gratify. It is common for aged spinsters to get a thrill out
of being afraid. They find looking under the bed or in the
closet for a man pleasurable.

This phenomenon also explains why children sit at the edge
of their seats, biting their nails, while watching a movie-
thriller; why grown-ups enjoy "roller-coaster" rides; why
some read morbid literature, and why others enjoy attending
funerals.

These individuals complain of psychosomatic aches and
pains, never associating them with their self-induced fears.

• The Hostility Motive

Feelings of hostility can be responsible for a multiplicity of
psychosomatic ailments.

There are individuals who become criminals because of
hatred of their father. They resent any kind of discipline or
authority. Law-and-order are symbolic of their dominating
father. Unfortunately they do not know that they are hitting
their heads against a brick wall. They invariably pay a price
one way or another; society punishes them, they punish themselves unconsciously by developing a host of health complaints, or both.

• The Attention-Getting Motive

We all like to feel that we are loved and wanted. We have
this basic need for affection. But unfortunately, some of us
are either deprived of the necessary amount of love and kindness from those close to us, or we have had too much attention paid to us as children.

• A Backache That Proved to Be a Heartache

An attractive young wife had made the rounds of doctors
in the community. She complained of a severe backache.
She had tried everything—massages, diathermy, hydrotherapy—but all in vain. In revealing her personal life to
me she admitted that her marriage was a disappointment.
Her husband, who had paid her so much attention during the
courtship, had neglected to make her feel *loved* following the
marriage ceremony. She had not considered it significant that
her backaches had begun in the first few months of her married life. The more she complained, the more her husband
worried about her. He would rub her back, take her to different doctors, and try to make her forget about her backaches by bringing her an occasional surprise gift.

Neurotic patients of this kind have a blindspot; they do
not know how their ailments are motivated, hence they remain ill indefinitely until the true cause of their complaint is
exposed.

• A Substitute for Mother Love

Together with this bid for attention—a substitute for mother
love—they develop a self-pity complex. They become martyrs
in search of listening ears in order that they may have an opportunity to tell of their many sacrifices, their ills and sorrows.
But in participating in this game of the unconscious, they fail
to realize that their neurotic symptoms handicap their ability
to relax, to enjoy life, or to succed in achieving goals that
would otherwise bring them happiness.

• How to Evaluate and Manage Your Health Complaints

If your doctor fails to find a physical cause for your ailments, then consider the possibility that they may be *psychosomatic,* of a self-punishment pattern. You are only hurting
yourself when you become a willing victim of evasive illness.
Try to find a hidden motive for your health complaints.

If you must carry an assortment of worries about with you,
park them well outside the dining room. *Fear* and *anger* can

cause *indigestion.* When eating, the mind should be relaxed and free of anything that tends to be upsetting. Discussions of an unpleasant nature should be avoided during mealtime, because they provide anxiety states which in turn cause indigestion. *Don't "talk shop" during lunch hour* if you have found from experience that it distresses you. Feed your mind pleasant thoughts while you are feeding your body.

Our modern tempo of restless living has speeded up our metabolism and consequently has altered our habits of eating, to the extent that thousands of us are suffering from "nervous stomachs."

Nervous indigestion is nothing more than a personal reaction to a situation that is *unpleasant.* It can be avoided through the application of a little mental hygiene.

Watch your eating habits. The average man has a tendency to become a glutton for delicacies and consumes more food than his body can use. Remember that obesity predisposes the body to such conditions as diabetes, hardening of the arteries, heart ailments, and various metabolic disturbances. That 20 extra pounds in weight is equivalent to carrying a twenty pound bar of iron every place you go.

No one envied the physique of either Mahatma Ghandi or Falstaff. Strike a happy medium and live in moderation by avoiding excesses. Resolve to eat *less.*

Avoid emotional conflicts. Bicarbonate of soda will not cure mental indigestion. If you wish to control your stomach, *learn to control your mind.*

Modify your personality-reactions to situational-frustrations.

Improve your physical health through emotional happiness.

Session 8.

~~~~~~

Nervous Fatigue: The
Great American Disease

• *What Is "Nervous Fatigue?"*

Nervous-fatigue is a body-mind phenomenon, far more prevalent today than even the common cold. Fatigue is a universal symptom. Our modern tempo of living and the chaotic conditions throughout the world are contributing causes. *Nervous tension* (inability to relax), associated with nervous fatigue is a handicap in life, affecting not only physical health but mental happiness.

• *Fatigue-Intoxication*

Whether you become exhausted after 18 holes of golf, an afternoon of shopping, or a day's work under pressure, the mechanism of fatigue is the same. Tiredness is a form of chemical intoxication brought on by the accumulation of "fatigue substances" that affect the entire nervous system and in turn alter the mental disposition of the individual. In excess you become *fatigue-drunk*. With adequate rest, the fatigue toxins are eliminated and you again become *sober*.

● *The Nervous Fatigue Syndrome*

There are many of us who strive to keep on going without giving our bodies the necessary chance to recuperate. Some complain of constantly feeling exhausted but cannot account for the source of their fatigue. In both groups we usually find this syndrome (combination of symptoms); exaggerated tiredness, insomnia, irritability, a multiplicity of physical ailments (headaches, digestive disorders, vague aches and pains) difficulty in concentrating, and disinclination for work. If you find yourself developing these symptoms, it should be a warning that you are approaching the stage of nervous fatigue. If unheeded, consequences may be serious.

● *Fatigue as a Warning Symptom*

At this point, an analogy may help emphasize what is meant by *consequences*. If you are driving a car at night and you begin to swerve off the road because you are tired and sleepy, you realize that it is sensible to stop and rest. The person who suffers a *nervous breakdown* is usually an individual who refuses to pause physically and mentally. He drives himself to a point of falling asleep at the wheel. The crash that follows is the result of his accumulated fatigue. Often the crash comes before one realizes its approach.

● *"Shattered Nerves"*

Janet, a woman of 35, complained of having lost her grip on life. "My nerves are shot," she said. "I'm tired all the time and don't know why. I don't sleep at night and every little thing seems to upset me. I just can't get hold of myself. I feel I'm headed for a breakdown. My husband thinks I'm neurotic."

There are thousands like Janet in the same predicament, helpless because they have never been taught how to avoid those things that consume nervous energy.

• Causes of Chronic Tiredness

Emotional conflicts and frustrations frequently cause nervous fatigue. *Bitterness, hostility,* and *resentment* can cause one to be excessively tired.

Thelma described how her father had bullied her when she was a child. She feared him and grew to despise his very presence. To make matters worse, her sister became abusive and tormented her. Exposure to such early influences produced desperate feelings of insecurity. What finally happened? She became obsessed with the idea that she could no longer look after her two children because of her headaches and general ill health. She claimed she had been *physically tired all of her life.* The tiredness was actually *nervous fatigue* caused by having to repress her resentment against her father and sister.

The sister was taking care of Thelma's two children. The woman's father paid the bills she incurred through her illness. Her husband became the father-substitute and victim of her hostility, with the result that she did not desire physical relations with him. Unconsciously, through her neurotic illness, she was getting revengeful satisfaction in making her father, sister, and husband pay for the mistreatment she received as a child.

But all this produced in Thelma a strong sense of guilt as evidenced by the occasional remark, "But doctor, I love my father and sister; at least I should." Her guilt was responsible for her self-hatred, which in turn made her entertain thoughts of suicide. In the meantime, while this vicious cycle continued, she became more *tired* and *unhappy* and was unable to function as a social human being, as a wife, or as a mother.

It was not until she had developed insight into the true cause of her chronic tiredness that she experienced relief from this nervous tension and fatigue.

• A Case of Neurasthenia

Another patient, Pauline, a woman in her late thirties, came to me complaining of *chronic fatigue.* She had con-

sulted many doctors believing her symptom was due to some
unrecognized illness. She experienced very little relief from
tonics and vitamins.

Members of her family were convinced that she was only
looking for sympathy. Unfortunately they told her they did
not want to be annoyed listening to her complain about always
being tired. Pauline felt that she had been rejected by her
family, that they did not understand her. She felt alone in
an "unsympathetic" world. She developed a defensive attitude
toward people, seldom smiled, and became suspicious of everyone. She accused her employer of discriminating against her;
she was jealous of her co-workers. She became increasingly
asocial. Finally she was advised to see a psychiatrist because
of her inefficiency at work and was given the ultimatum of
either getting herself straightened out or having to resign.

Pauline related how she had been subjected to many in-
justices throughout her life. She wept, saying she never knew
how it felt to be liked by someone. Later it developed she had
always been a "prude," afraid to make friends with the opposite sex, fearing complications. She feared all men, feared
that she might be disappointed were she to fall in love, and
felt sure she would never be able to accept the intimate responsibilities that go with marriage. She sought sanctity,
shut herself in a furnished room, worked all day, occasionally
attended a movie at night, and devoted her leisure time to
reminding herself how *tired* she was. She expressed pride in
the fact that she was a "good" person.

Pauline was brought to realize that she had fallen into a
neurotic rut, that her fanatic prudishness was stunting her
emotional and social growth, and that she was suffering from
a case of *neurasthenia*, which manifested itself in the form of
chronic fatigue. She finally took a sensible attitude toward
love and marriage and entered into a courtship with someone
who planned to marry her. She became practical, learned to
dance, swim, and drive a car. Determinedly, she took a course
in personality development, changed the way she wore her
hair and bought clothes that were more becoming. The change

was so remarkable that her friends insisted that this new person must surely be her twin-sister whom they had never met. Everyone spoke about what a nice person she had become.

Convinced that her fatigue had not been caused by any organic condition, Pauline realized for the first time that her symptom of *chronic tiredness* was symbolic of the attitude she assumed toward everything and everyone around her.

• *Emotionalism Can Make You Tired*

Anger, hatred, jealousy, sorrow, anxiety, envy, and crying spells are expressions of *emotionalism*. They are abnormal reactions giving rise to *emotional intoxication*. They dissipate one's mental strength and, in turn, cause *physical fatigue*. A spell of the "blues" can tire one more quickly than actual labor. Emotional disturbances arising out of family dissentions, marital incompatibility, financial difficulties, and sexual excesses and maladjustments, as well as disappointments in love, all have a tendency to exhaust one both physically and mentally.

• *Occupational Boredom*

Working at something you don't particularly like or are not fitted for, gives rise to fatigue and mental stagnation. It isn't because you spend eight to ten hours a day working that you are exhausted. It is because you exercise the same few muscles all day long, with neglect of the other muscles of your body. The monotony of mechanical living, doing the same thing day in and day out—coming home, eating, feeling tired, and going to bed early—is bound to have a demoralizing effect.

• *What about Overwork?*

It isn't the amount of work you do but the *manner* in which you do that work that is tiring. John, for example, boasts of how busy he keeps himself at his place of business. When John comes home, he is peevish, complains to his wife of how "worn out" he feels. He wonders why he doesn't get a raise in salary. His error is in thinking that keeping frantically busy means working efficiently. Unfortunately, John hasn't learned the secret of *emotional economy,* doing things in a relaxed way.

● *Fears Can Exhaust You*

Harboring morbid and absurd fears means working your mind overtime. They wear you out and rob you of both physical and mental strength.

● *Miscellaneous Factors Associated with Fatigue*

Irregular living, improper food, overeating, loss of sleep, lack of exercise, and absence of recreational outlets, all help to bring about a state of mental sluggishness and chronic tiredness.

● *What You Can Do to Be Less Tired*

Use these specific techniques to overcome nervous fatigue.

1. To begin with, don't decide for yourself that your fatigue is *mental,* not physical. *Let your physician decide.* Get a medical survey of yourself. Fatigue may be an early symptom of such conditions as tuberculosis, heart disease, anemia, diabetes, glandular disturbances, chronic constipation, infectious conditions (colds, bad teeth, rheumatism, boils, and sinus trouble). They all can contribute to that tired feeling. If you have an ailment that needs to be treated, do something about it. If, after a careful check-up by your physician, no evidence can be found of any illness, then you may safely conclude your fatigue is due to *psychological* causes.

2. Relax mentally. Keep your mind relaxed and free of any unpleasantness that tends to keep you upset. Try to get along with the people you have to work with. *Unhappiness* causes you to be *chronically depressed* and constitutes one of the major causes of nervous fatigue. An optimistic philosophy of life will aid you in control-

ling your emotions, and this in turn will conserve
your energy. Don't subject yourself to emotional
outbursts. Fear and hate are fatigue-produc-
ing.

3. The average individual requires eight hours of
sleep. Sleep is nature's way of building up
energy. Don't cheat yourself. It's too expensive.
Be sensible about your living habits.

4. Keep in mind that recreation is *mental medicine*. A variety of diversion every week is desirable. Breaking away from the grind occasionally. Exercising dormant muscles and re-
freshing one's thoughts restores energy.

5. If you have a sitting job and one that is monotonous at that, seek outdoor recreation in tennis.
golf, fishing, hunting, swimming, dancing, or
hiking. They are mental vitamins. If your job
requires constant use of your arms or legs, seek
mental relaxation through bridge, the theatre,
automobile riding, or reading.

6. Take an interval rest-period during working
hours whenever possible. It gives your body and
mind a breathing spell.

7. Before leaving work learn to lock your troubles
in your desk drawer.

8. Don't try to crowd into a day's program more
than you can accomplish well. Working in excess
of a reasonable number of hours is equivalent to
overeating. It causes psychic-indigestion.

9. Work in rhythm by learning to do things *well*
in the *easiest* way.

10. Take things in their natural stride.

11. Budget your energy as you budget your money.
Don't squander it.

12. When you come home from work, take a half-
hour nap if you're tired, followed by a stimulating shower. Rest is a sure-cure for fatigue-ir-
ritability.

13. *Stop running.* Everyone seems to be in a hurry.
Hurry brings on excessive fatigue. Slow down.
You last longer. Give yourself time to get your
second wind.

14. Find out what gives you a "lift." It may be a highball or two before dinner, a movie after dinner, a visit with the neighbors, or a week-end trip some place. What relaxes the mind, relaxes the body. Live a well-rounded life.

15. Stop *reminding* yourself and others how tired you are. Complaining makes you even more tired. Doing something about it is the better solution.

16. Keep your life *simple*. Don't complicate it with more activities than you can handle.

17. Avoid the *worry-habit*. Don't get worked up over something that will never happen. I have had patients who worried when they didn't worry. Don't be one of them. Worry is energy-consuming. That reminds me of a colleague who explained the difference between one who is psychotic and one who is neurotic by stating that the psychotic or insane person believes 2 and 2 make *5* while the neurotic knows that 2 and 2 are *4,* but *he worries about it.*

▀▬▬▀▬▬▀▬▬▀▬▬▀▬▬▀▬▬▀▬▬▀▬▬▀▬▬▀▬▬▀▬▬▀▬▬▀▬▬▀▬▬▀▬▬▀▬▬▀

Personality-Halitosis
And Its Remedy

● *Personality-Rigidity*

Stubbornness is a personality-liability—something most of us dislike. It is a form of *personality-rigidity*. There is nothing so obnoxious as the person who is always right, never compromises, and is happiest when he can get into a hot, unreasonable argument. He never admits his shortcomings, he is never wrong.

Narrow-mindedness and political and religious fanaticism are forms of stubbornness. We shun people who are dogmatic, rigid, unable to appreciate the other person's point of view.

A boat must be evenly balanced to assure safety. It is far better to sit in the middle than to lean dangerously to one side or the other. One of the surest ways to alienate a friend is to give the impression that you cannot be convinced about anything—that you are a *bull-headed* crank.

● *The Chip-on-the-Shoulder Crank*

Irritability is another undesirable trait. This *chip-on-the-shoulder* type of crank has a *defensive* personality. He doubts the sincerity of his friends, is easily offended, and resents any criticism. One disparaging word, and he explodes. His irritability is due to his dissatisfaction with himself, and he expresses it by *projecting* his inner unhappiness on to others. He uses this mechanism to dissipate his unconscious, pent-up self-hatred. Someone else has to suffer for his sorrows.

It is the *unhappy* who are generally cranky, belligerent, and hard to get along with. The happy, well-integrated human being may show occasional irritability; he has his off-days, but his upset never becomes chronic. He shakes off other people's abusiveness and won't allow them to make him unhappy. He has found that it is easier to get along with everyone than to get along with only a particular few. The wise man never allows himself to be swept away by his emotions. He has cultivated the habit of *self-control*.

• The Egocentric Crank

Self-centeredness (egoism) is still another personality-handicap. Everything is appraised in terms of "How does it affect me?" His is strictly a "What can I gain?" attitude. He is constantly thinking about the clothes he wears, what he eats, how people take to him, wondering if various organs of his body are functioning properly. He is usually worried about his constipation. The wise doctor tells him he is suffering from "egoitis." He becomes interested, believing he has some new disease which no one else has. When he learns that "egoitis" is a special term for "self-centeredness"—too much "I"—a *personality-disease* rather than a physical illness, he is indignant at the classification.

In this group are the conceited, the vain, and the selfish. This type is an *egocentric crank*. The world moves only around him. He fails to realize that he is but one of two billion people inhabiting an earth twenty-four thousand miles in circumference, just a speck in the great wide world.

If he is married, his wife is expected to conform to all of his plans. He marries for convenience, for the gratification of his hunger and sex instincts. He likes to bully his wife; gives vent to outbursts of profanity and anger and thinks a woman's activities should be confined to the kitchen and bedroom of her home. If he engages in a quarrel, he is always right. Company bores him. His selfishness is manifested in his desire to be loved and respected without doing any loving himself.

He believes in a European master-slave relationship. If he slips and philanders, he expects to be forgiven and rationalizes his infidelity with some flimsy excuse. But should his wife make some innocent gesture of affection toward a friend at a party, he becomes insanely jealous. He understands little about a woman's emotions. If he happens to be handsome, his conceit becomes intolerable. If he's a "big-shot" in business, politics, or his profession, he expects to be treated like a big-shot at home.

A moderate amount of egoism and pride are normal. However, excess vanity, overestimation of self, and conceit are defects in an intolerable personality.

• *Over-sensitivity*

If you take a boxer's stance—mentally—as soon as people come around, they are going to feel uncomfortable with you. That is what the *oversensitive* person does. He throws up defenses before they're needed or retires hurt and weeping from slights, real or imagined.

Others are human just as you are. You forget insults you yourself administer and remember only the apparent indifference and callousness of others. The wife who weeps whenever her husband gets out of hand is apt to find herself left to her sorrow. It doesn't pay to be oversentimental.

We all know couples who constantly bicker over trivialities, each oversensitive, on the defensive. Their relationship is like a melody played in a discordant key.

• *The Health Crank*

The health-complainer enjoys describing his many ailments. Yet there is nothing so unpleasant as to hear someone forever complaining about his health. It's either a headache, indigestion, neuralgia, pains, or a past, perhaps future, operation.

Two people can be sick with a cold. One will take his prescribed medicine, stay in bed, follow the doctor's instructions, and wait for his physician and nature to cure him. This is a normal reaction to illness. The other fellow anxiously asks a thousand and one questions. He wants to know if his cold may develop into pneumonia, if it's all right to smoke or to stay out of bed for a little while. He has heard of a good old fashioned remedy for a cold and should he try it. He's uncooperative, grouchy, demands a lot of attention. Nurses recognize such a patient as a *health crank*.

• *The Chronic Complainer*

There are others who forever complain about their job. The work is monotonous, they feel they are worth more than their salary, the boss is unreasonable, or the job has no future. It's not unusual for example to hear a government worker exclaim: "I file cards all day long. I haven't learned a thing. My job is so monotonous I feel like screaming."

They are reminded that even though they are only a small cog in the wheel, they can do much toward working for a better position by improving their qualifications. Many government workers attend evening courses at various universities, strengthening their knowledge in their own field or acquiring new skills. Why should anyone stagnate in a world such as ours?

The chronic complainer, because of his own inner discontentment, makes everyone else miserable. No one understands the cause of his continual unhappiness. He is unpopular. No one guesses he is an emotionally frustrated person, and so he is despised as a "pain in the neck," an unbearable whiner.

He wonders why he's never a guest the second time. The girl he wants finds an excuse to be out when he calls. At work, he keeps waiting for the raise that fails to come through.

He has a blind spot. Everyone is out of step but Johnny. While he may be vaguely aware of possessing a personality that fails to gain friendships, he lacks insight into the reasons why he differs from other people. He is never able to hold a job or a friendship. There seems to be something wrong with his personality make-up.

• *You Can't Afford to Be Belligerent and Sarcastic*

A patient told me: "I'm about to call it quits. I hate everyone and I even hate myself. There is absolutely no reason for living. I haven't any friends. I don't like my job, I have no interest in anything. I'm here only because I haven't the courage to commit suicide. I'm afraid to die, but I can't go on living a life that's so empty and hopeless. I just can't stand it."

When asked why she had no friends, she said, "I suppose it's my own fault. I'm sarcastic and belligerent most of the time. They call me 'Old Sour-Puss' because I never smile. I just can't be nice to people. And I can't pretend to be happy when I'm not. But I've gone through so much! It's no wonder I go around with a chip on my shoulder."

I was curious to learn about the unfortunate past that accounted for this attitude. I discovered that her brother had teased her practically all of her life. He was mean and was responsible for her early feelings of inferiority. Her parents bickered continuously. The home environment was bad. There was never any demonstration of affection among any of the members of the family.

But this was not all. She had been injured in an automobile accident. As a result, she now walks with a noticeable limp. The greatest damage was not the physical impairment, but the emotional repercussions of her accident. She was no longer able to dance. Her inability to reconcile herself to her affliction, and her conviction that she would never find the love and happiness to which every woman is entitled became a source of great frustration.

This girl subconsciously decided to take out on the world the unhappiness she suffered at the hands of her parents, her brother, and all who had been, as she expressed it, "damned cruel" to her.

Individuals with physical afflictions are either very friendly and easy to get along with, or they acquire *ugly* dispositions.

When this patient was made to see herself in a true light, she resolved to assume a more positive and wholesome attitude toward herself and others. She ultimately became a likeable person.

• *Develop Your Personality*

Once upon a time, we used to feel that personality was an indefinable something that certain people had and others lacked. We know now, quite conclusively, that personality *can* be developed. And the development of personality depends upon learning to do an increasing number of things *with and for other people.*

"As our personality expands," asserts Dr. Henry C. Link, "our happiness also expands." This is not a new philosophy. We have always known but too often neglected this simple truth.

"The secret of a growing personality and happiness," contines Dr. Link, "is the determination to form new habits and to embark on new adventures. . . . The person who, because of fear, stops trying new approaches to people, will never expand his understanding or love of people, and his happiness, instead of growing, will shrink."[1]

Dr. Link tells a story that has been many times repeated in the experiences of every psychologist and psychiatrist. A middle-aged business woman suffered terrific fits of depression. As these spells became more frequent, her work suffered badly. An investigation confirmed the suspicion that this woman had a very limited circle of acquaintances and virtually no friends. Although she had worked with certain employees for years, she knew almost nothing about them. She was advised to study the people about her, to learn something of their work and their families. This she did and at the last report she was so engrossed in helping two families that she had no time for melancholy reflections. As Dr. Link puts it, "Having given herself to others, she no longer needed to get away from herself." In helping others to achieve happiness, she found it for herself.

---

[1] Dr. Henry C. Link, *The Return to Religion* (New York: Macmillan Co., 1936).

The answer to personality-halitosis is not to stay away from people, but to analyze your deficiencies and correct them. You can cultivate the kind of personality-qualities that will make you win friends.

• *Insight*

Literally speaking, "insight" means "to look within." A person with a normal insight is one who, after a careful self-examination, has acquired a better perspective on life in general and knows exactly how he stands, by way of comparison with the rest of the world.

Like ostriches with heads buried in the sand, many of us cannot see around us. As the Bible says, "We have eyes and we see not, have ears and we hear not, have hands and we feel not, we have brains and we think not."

How many of us really *think?* Most of the things we do are done through *habit.* Understanding yourself, other people and the world we live in is *real* thinking.

By developing insight you can analyze your faults, correct them, cultivate personal magnetism, and, in general, master the art of *getting along.*

A knowledge of your inner-self is one of the most important requisites for the development of a successful personality.

If eight out of ten people think you're a "pill," a "snake-in-the-grass," a "pain-in-the-neck," a "flat tire," or the "horse's neck," *do* something about it. Overhaul your personality. Have some consideration for other people's feelings. Don't expect the world to change its entire course for your benefit.

• *Poise*

Another important personality-attribute, developed usually from a feeling of self-confidence, is *poise.*

It is as difficult to define poise as it is to describe space. Perhaps Kipling has best succeeded, in his well-remembered poem, "If."

"If you can keep your head when all about you
are losing theirs and blaming it on you,"
—then at least you are well on the way toward the acquisition
of poise.

Persons who lack self-composure envy those who own the
virtue and ability to remain serene through adversities.

Temperamental *decisions* result from a confusion of facts
and oftentimes prove costly. Soundness of judgment can only
come from a feeling of *self-assurance.*

The world applauds the individual who displays *personality-
finesse,* who has a firm grip on life and an accurate estimation
of his merits, and who can cover his virtues under a cloak of
modesty.

● *Ambition*

Ambition, if properly managed, is another personality asset.
To live without inspiration of noble aspirations is to live a
life of drudgery. The impelling urge to achieve and to lift
ourselves above the commonplace things of life is present in
all of us. Rational ambition is the vehicle and driving force
that transports directed energy toward the best for accomplishment. Persons who mistake desire for capacity usually
end in failure because of their misdirected ambition.

When ambition exceeds ability, unhappiness is the inevitable result. There's virtue in reaching for the stars, but
it's far more practical to attain the small things in life first.

Achieve one goal at a time. It took a skilled Roman to hold
the reins of six horses and win a chariot race. Unless you have
the right grip on more than one set of reins in life, you are
unlikely to take the sharp curves without *upsetting.*

Many of our failures we can attribute to never finishing
the thing we start. We lack the ability to concentrate on a
project long enough to realize its accomplishment.

Persons concentrating their efforts toward the achievement
of one goal at a time may find inspiration in an old Italian
proverb: "The world steps aside to let any man pass who
knows whither he is going."

Educate your mind. Acquire as much culture as you can. Public libraries, free concerts, and museums of art and science constitute the dividends of a poor man's bank account.

What food is to the body, culture is to the mind. Select some absorbing leisure interest in your program of self-education, whether it be literature, music, or art.

Education of the soul is essential to happiness and can be obtained any time, anywhere, and at any age. As George Horace Lorimer said:

> You'll find that education is about the only thing lying around loose in this world, and that it's about the only thing a fellow can have as much of as he is willing to haul away. Everything else is screwed down tight and the screw-driver lost.[2]

• *Stick-to-itiveness*

Develop the ability to *persevere*. To persevere is to develop enough will-power to overcome weakness of determination and to enable you to attain the completion of started plans.

Napoleon once said, "Victory belongs to the most persevering." The power of perseverance may be found in the biographies of many great men.

Despite the nature of your obstacles, you are actually beaten only when you acknowledge defeat and failure. A guitar player who discontinues his music lessons because he finds it difficult to finger a particular chord will never become a musician.

We all have undiscovered talents of some kind buried in the grey matter of our brain. It takes perseverance and energy to develop them.

• *Tactfulness*

Be sure that your *conversation* is not a liability to you. There are persons who think it is best to be painfully honest and express their thoughts rather than suppress them. These are the would-be righteous who so often are heard to say: "I

---

[2] John W. Tebbel, *George Horace Lorimer and the Saturday Evening Post* (Doubleday, Garden City, N. Y., 1948).

told him to his face." or "You asked for it—this is what I
think." Launching verbal knives at friends isn't being honest.
It is in many cases a self-satisfied form of *sadism*.

You don't have to tell your hostess the meat is tough. You
can simply keep quiet about it without impairing your honesty. Those who are *sarcastic* and bent on embarrassing others
soon find themselves *friendless*. Girls who try to build themselves up on a date by talking about their other men friends
are more than tactless—they are foolhardy. They brand
themselves as vain, repel the men they go out with, and possibly cut themselves off from the very love they seek.

• Get to Like People

Not all of us find we can be *diplomatic*. But we can all be
kind. Control that impulse to say the cutting thing, the "truth"
that will leave a barb of hurt. You can cultivate the ability
to engage in interesting conversation. The first thing you
need to do is to *like* people. If you like people your interests
will enlarge and your field of friendship will expand. It is
people who make music, make love, make life. Once you grasp
that, you will inevitably find your interest quicken; you will
keep in touch with what goes on in your world, not because it
is required, but because its fascinating.

Gloom is *contagious*. It rubs off on the other person, and,
remembering it, he avoids you the next time. Make your conversation grow out of your own life's fullness, and you will
listen out of liking and interest for the other fellow. It is
magnetic.

• Don't Put Yourself in a Bad Light

If you have any fanatic obsessions about love, religion, sex,
or life in general, try to clear them up as quickly as you can.
In any event, don't advertise them among your friends.

One of my patients could not resist telling her men friends
about the emotional difficulties that made it necessary for her
to seek the help of a psychiatrist. The result was inevitable.

She put up her own quarantine sign for keeping men away.
We all know others—the religious fanatic, the Aryan fanatic,
the intolerant in all walks of life.

● *Intolerance Warps Your Personality*

Learn to be tolerant of others. After all they have to tolerate
you. Your own intolerance and antagonisms will repel would-
be friends or lovers like a charged wire. As soon as they touch
on one of your pet hates, the charge strikes; they are unlikely
to come back for more.

● *Ten Suggestions for Winning Friends*

If you want to cure yourself of personality-halitosis, here is
the remedy. Resolve that from this day on you are going to:

1. Keep your complaints down to a minimum;
2. Avoid bickering and quarreling;
3. Be tactful and tolerant;
4. Be courteous and understanding;
5. Improve your personal appearance;
6. Avoid conceit;
7. Learn to mind your own business;
8. Be appreciative and unselfish;
9. Be cheerful, and congenial;
10. *Be a friend.*

Session 10.

░░

Overcome Your
Inferiority Complex

• *Everyone Has Feelings of Inferiority*

Who hasn't felt inferior? We all have to some extent, if for no other reason than being aware that we can all *improve*.

What do we know about the mysterious forces of Nature? We are all born eventually to die and are unable to do much about it. Our life is but a small cogwheel in a gigantic machine of perpetual living. This alone makes one feel helpless and inferior. It is this feeling of intellectual helplessness that inspires scientists of the world to challenge the secrets of the Universe. The discovery of the atomic bomb is the latest evidence of the ingenuity of man's mind—an attempt to conquer the elements, a striving for power.

Douglas Lurton in his book *Make the Most of Your Life* [1] tells how his friend and former associate Guy Hickok came to the realization that people great and small are so nearly alike that no one needs to feel inferior in the presence of another.

Rich or poor, we are all exposed to the same disappointments, threats, illnesses, storms, accidents, and wars. Our

---

[1] Douglas Lurton, *Make the Most of Your Life*. Garden City Books, 1953.

94

best defense is to build up an inner immunity against their effect on our morale. To accomplish this we start with the confidence that we can survive physically and emotionally the painful realities of life. If others can do it, we can too.

• Self-Pity Destroys Self-Confidence

Nine out of ten persons suffer from *self-pity*. There are many who because of some physical handicap, experience greater feelings of inferiority than the more fortunate. They become victims of bitterness and self-pity.

The history of a patient comes to mind, illustrating how an inferiority complex that developed from an acquired physical handicap became the root of his premature ageing, narcotic addition, and final insanity.

James, a painter by trade, married and the father of a handsome boy, is now an inmate of a mental institution. He was subjected to an amputation at the hip joint of the right leg. Following his operation he developed a chronic osteomyelitis of the hip bone and has been an ill-fated victim of a recurrence of agonizing symptoms since the onset of his misfortune. He soon developed a very noticeable inferiority complex and sought refuge as a nomadic neurotic by traveling from one hospital to another. He has made several attempts at suicide, has become addicted to narcotics, and was declared psychotic and incompetent by a board of psychiatrists.

For years James had made his physical handicap his sole interest in life. He has drifted into a private world of his own, steeped in self-pity.

• A Physical Handicap Can Give You a Greater Urge to Succeed

Most of us overcompensate for our handicaps by working that much harder toward the attainment of a worthwhile goal. There are innumerable examples of persons whose individual handicaps or afflictions have given them the impetus to achieve more than average success. The late Franklin D. Roosevelt refused to allow a physical impediment to interfere with his ambitions. Helen Keller, Beethoven, Edison, and a host of others could well leave us the philosophical legacy, "Be glad you feel inferior"—if your inferiority feelings give you a greater will to achieve.

● Psychic Invalidism

But there are others, the over-sensitive, whose inferiorities block their paths to success. Not satisfied with one handicap they complicate matters by taking on an added burden—a self-pity type of invalidism. We say the individual suffers from a superimposed neurosis, equivalent to having two diseases at one time. A good example is a gangster who in hating himself because he looks like a "thug" (due to a malformed nose or cauliflower ear) sets out on a campaign to make society suffer for something for which it is not to blame. Unable to fight Fate, his real opponent, this maladjusted mental cripple takes it out on society—his substitute sparring partner.

● Self-Pity Can Make You Physically Ill

Not long ago an attorney, 42 years of age, told me he had completely lost confidence in himself, claiming he had always had an inferiority complex. His wife believed he was taking his work too seriously. He complained of terrific headaches, nervousness, and indigestion. He became irritable over trivialities and worried needlessly about his domestic responsibilities.

A psychiatric evaluation of his symptoms disclosed feelings of self-pity, which were brought to the surface through analysis.

He ultimately overcame his feelings of inferiority and assumed a brighter outlook on life, having realized that his mind and body were an integral unit and that his self-pity was causing him to feel physically ill and was accentuating his inferiority complex.

● Its Selfish to Feel Inferior

No matter how many different ways you analyze the psychology of neurotic inferiority, you'll arrive at a common denominator—selfishness. Put it to the test. Trace your feelings of inferiority to their origin. Subject yourself to a retrospective analysis (a reliving of your life), and you'll discover that you have been wasting a lot of energy fighting a misfortune of Fate. No one has ever been able to undo the work of Fate (for example, giving themselves new parents and new childhoods, or changing the color of their skins or their lines of descent); to attempt to do so is like beating one's head against a wailing-wall.

• Negative Overcompensation

Margaret related how many times she had felt humiliated because she wasn't as pretty as her sister. Her neurotic mother reminded her of the difference and pointed out to relatives and friends how much she looked like her father, a particularly unattractive man.

She became extremely self-conscious and decided the only way to hold a boy friend was to make a physical concession. She became promiscuous and, because of her feelings of guilt, began to deaden her remorse by drinking to excess. Margaret went from inferiority to promiscuity, from guilt to alcohol, and only deepened her feelings of inferiority. She felt sunken to a helpless degree and didn't know where to begin to straighten herself out. In her own words, she found herself "swimming in a whirlpool of confused emotions."

Holding up the psychoanalytic mirror, she finally saw the distressing reflection of her other self. There are thousands like Margaret, resorting to some form of *negative overcompensation* for their inferiority feelings.

• Lack of Self-Discipline

People in describing their feelings of inferiority tell you how they find it almost impossible to carry out instructions regarding disciplinary measures they can take to develop confidence. It requires effort to overcome any kind of complex. But the *self-pitier* wants a simple way out, because he is selfish in addition to feeling inferior. He is unwilling to suffer physical or mental discomfort for the sake of achieving his goal. He wants to enter an obstacle race without having to jump the hurdles.

• *Inferiority in Reverse: A False Sense of Superiority*

Most every neurotic suffers from an inferiority complex. Some admit it, and others deny it. The latter quite often claim they feel *superior* to most people. But this sense of superiority in itself is evidence in disguise of feelings of inferiority. As Dr. Alfred Adler, world-famous psychologist and founder of this theory expressed it, "Behind everyone who behaves as if he was superior to others, we can suspect a feeling of inferiority which calls for very special efforts of concealment."

• *The Need to Be Loved*

The need for love is present not only in neurotics, but in all of us. Few of us realize that love must be *earned*. To receive love we must be capable of giving love. Love isn't just hugs and kisses. It is a condition of the mind, a sense of inner tranquility that communicates itself to others. The happiest among us are those who radiate *self-confidence*. An inferiority complex may be the explanation for one's failure to find love or to make marriage a success.

One need not search the far corners of the earth to find love. The capacity to love is present in the soul of everyone. But like the absent-minded professor who searches for his spectacles only to discover that he has them on, we seek everywhere except within ourselves.

• *An Inferiority Complex Repels Love*

A patient, a young lady of 34, told me the other day, "What I need, Doctor, is someone to love me, a home and children like other people. It would cure me of my *inferiority complex.*

"You're putting the cart before the horse," I informed her. "The question is . . . just how lovable are you?"

I learned that she had many suitors, but apparently was unable to hold any of them. She either tried to make them jealous or said the wrong thing. In one instance, she became reckless and played her last card by suggesting marriage to a man who was shy and inhibited, and wound up by frightening him away. Her last suitor entered the service, wrote a few letters, and then faded out of the picture.

"Would she be an old maid?" That was the fear that haunted her. Like thousands of other women she was under the impression that love would someday come her way out of nowhere, and that she would live happily with her Prince Charming ever after.

I had her look into a mirror and tell me what she saw. The reflected image showed eyes that were cloudy with discontent. Lips tight with bitterness. Her whole expression betrayed a woman who had forgotten how to smile.

She appeared surprised when I told her that one prepares for love by becoming self-reliant. This preparing process begins in childhood. Unfortunately, parents condition children to so much unhappiness in many instances that when they grow up to be adults they feel *inferior*. Threatened by inner fears of inadequacy, they are incapable of developing a normal love relationship toward the opposite sex. They grow up to be unloved neurotics. They unknowingly spite their parents and themselves by taking out on others the lovelessness and unhappiness of their childhood. In adult life they develop an insatiable hunger for affection and at the same time an *inferiority complex* that repels love.

• *Men Who Feel Inferior*

Many men who feel *inferior* become convinced that they are not getting the love and attention they need. They crave it and they don't know how to get it. Some are ashamed of this need and often refuse to recognize it consciously. So they develop a grievance against the world for failing to appreciate them.

This aggravated feeling finds its outlets. The man who feels he's being passed over at his job, for instance, gives vent to his suffering ego at home.

Such a case was the subject of a Broadway play not too long ago. A clerk of small means had completely lost hope of advancement. He loved his wife and daughter, but coming home to them was only a reminder of how poorly he was able to provide. So he blew up in furious irritation at the smallest item on the grocery or telephone bill and made life very unpleasant for his wife, his daughter, and the cat.

His angry outbursts seemed to be evidence of ill temper, but actually they were cries of fear and inferiority and disappointment at his own inability to cope with life. A hard man to live with? Yes. But fortunately in his case, his wife never lost sight of his lovable qualities and dogged efforts. Together they turned even the loss of his precariously held job into a moral triumph for his hurt pride.

The man with an inferiority complex may drive himself and his family into a frenzy in his determination to push himself ahead in his work, to win attention. Or he may turn to escape —through alcohol or flirtations, or in a hobby that will absorb him so completely he can't think about his humiliating standstill at work.

He may take refuge from a hostile world through sickness and turn his grievance into hypochondria. This he will not do deliberately, of course, but he may drift gradually and unconsciously into the comforting excuse.

With his eyes fixed only on his own self-invited inferiority, the neurotic individual sees all *his* problems as practically insurmountable, but all *yours* as trivial. In fact, he doesn't recognize yours as problems at all.

• *Essential Steps in the Cure of Inferiority*

1. If you feel inferior find out *why*. Use this a-b-c approach by asking yourself these questions.
    (a) What are some of the whys and wherefores of my feelings of inferiority? How did my inferiority complex come about? Am I trying to achieve an unattainable goal?
    (b) Have I been resorting to negative forms of over-compensation?
    (c) What disciplinary steps can I take to eliminate the handicap of feeling inferior?
2. A second step toward being cured is to have a conscious recognition of your major limitation or deficiency. Don't try to dodge it.

3. When you have found the clue to your inferiority via enlightened self-analysis, find an answer to it. Becoming resourceful and more successful through extra effort. Cooperating and contributing your bit toward keeping the wheels of civilization going may not bring you complete happiness, but it will act as a prophylaxis against *brain-idleness*. *Soul-satisfying* outlets in music, reading, art, literature, sports, are specific remedies for inferiority feelings. Self-denunciation solves nothing. The girl who stays away from dances because she is self-conscious about her figure is making it more difficult for herself to ultimately overcome her inferiority complex. Becoming an excellent dancer will rid her of that particular anxiety. Incidentally one person out of every three is disturbed because of marked self-consciousness.

4. Don't worry about having to *impress* people. Adopt a relaxed attitude. Be your real "you." It's the secret of feeling at ease around people.

5. Avoiding the things you dislike only deepens your feeling of inferiority. You can't overcome social shyness or awkwardness by being a stay-at-home. Get to meet people. Every person is a new book. Let them unconsciously read to you the chapters of their lives. Study people. It's a fascinating hobby, but be careful—no one wants to be a dissected guinea pig.

6. Stop walking backward. If you do nothing else, stand still until you are able to take a step forward. Remember that self-reliance comes with acceptance of responsibilities.

7. If you want to *feel* big—*think* big.

8. Convince yourself that you *get* what you *give.*

9. Decide what you *want* out of life. Go after it.

10. Develop the *will to achieve*—the determination to live a richer, happier life.

11. Don't build a wall around yourself.

12. Start a self-improvement notebook. Keep a record of your progress. Time spent in self-development is time well spent.

$\mathcal{S}$ession 11.

▄▀

Nervous Breakdowns
Can Be Prevented

● *What Is a "Nervous Breakdown?"*

A nervous breakdown is a state in which certain emotional conflicts interfere with the individual's ability to continue the normal routine of living. It also refers to a state of physical and mental exhaustion and is generally associated with such symptoms as an inability to continue working, loss of one's confidence, feelings of anxiety and panic, insomnia, fear of being alone, a sense of unreality, fear of insanity, chronic tiredness, depressed moods, thoughts of suicide, preoccupation with one's health, weeping spells, a disinterest in everything, and other similar patterns of thinking and behaving.

● *Precipitating Causes*

Nervous breakdowns are the outgrowth of inordinate *self-concern*. We are all under the strain of life's hardships, and we can use either destructive or constructive means to meet that strain.

A nervous breakdown is evidence that something went wrong in our emotional development. If a building is erected properly, it should withstand the average storms. But if the bricklayers use inferior materials and neglect certain rules of

102

construction, we can expect a collapse. Fortunately we have building inspectors and building laws that protect the occupants of the building. But we have no one checking up on parents to see that they have done a good construction job in bringing up their children.

A major frustration, such as disappointment in love, financial bankruptcy, sexual difficulty, grief, marital discord, divorce, loss of a job, or failure in a career, can cause one to suffer a nervous breakdown. The type of individual, however, who is most susceptible is one who is oversensitive, has never developed the art of *equanimity,* and is inclined to take himself and his troubles too seriously. He is prone to indulge in feelings of *self-pity.*

The high emotional tensions of our life today is the cause of a number of breakdowns.

The mind can also be hurt just as our bodies can. There are all kinds of mental wounds and injuries capable of producing emotional reactions that sometimes lead to a breakdown.

• *Grief: a Mental Wound*

A very common mental injury, one that we all experience sooner or later, is *grief.*

People react differently to sorrow. Some become hysterical; others take on a stoical or philosophical attitude; still others become depressed and mentally ill as a consequence.

Sally, a girl of 23, came to my office at the insistence of her sister. When I asked her what her complaint-problem was, she said:

"My sister thinks I am having a nervous breakdown and need the help of a psychiatrist. I have no appetite for food and I am rapidly losing weight. I don't sleep, and my friends tell me I am wasting away, that I'm beginning to look like a mental case. Nothing interests me anymore.

"You see, Doctor, I was engaged to a handsome boy several years ago, but my Bill lost his life in a plane crash. So my dreams never materialized. Why did this have to happen to me? I've lost my faith in everything, including my religion and God. Life has no meaning for me now. Food has no taste. Why should I be concerned about my health? The one thing that keeps me from ending it all is the fact that it would grieve my parents. In our family we are known for our ability to withstand hard knocks, but I must be the exception."

• The Adjustment Problem of a Widow

Only after many visits was she convinced that grief, like a physical wound, will heal. I tried to point out to her that the overwhelming sorrow of the widow, especially if she has been married for many years, is more justified than that of the promised bride. Over a span of years she has been the lesser half of a partnership. She has been protected, guided, and cared for in ill-health. She has been made to feel a dependency and a certain security. Suddenly she is launched into a competitive world to fend for herself. It is like a hand-worker suddenly losing his right arm. Some widows are able to make an adjustment, especially if they are left with loving children, ample financial standing, or both. Often these widows enter their children's homes and create havoc there.

A greater problem is the widow left without sufficient funds who has to earn her living for the first time in her life. Often she is (or thinks she is) quite unprepared.

• Grief May Be Self-Pity

However, if the widow continues to bear a torch, unable to find a place for herself in the world, she builds up a neurosis of utter selfishness and egoism. She may think that she is mourning for a beloved husband (and she is), but more than that she is mourning for friendship, comfort, and security. Her grief, which after a time should have brought some forgetting, is centered around herself. Unless she can be brought to a realization of her self-centering thoughts and bring new interests into her life, she will become hopelessly neurotic.

• Don't Hold Back Your Tears

In the event of the death of some member of your family,

a good cry is natural. It is better to express sorrow than to repress it, provided you don't become hysterical and make a spectacle of yourself. I've witnessed a good many funerals where some survivor would pull her hair and scream at the closing of the coffin. Behavior of this kind is abnormal. The dramatic display of sorrow is sometimes prompted by feelings of guilt. We wish to show our friends how grief-stricken we are, lest they accuse us of being indifferent; or we begin to think of the occasions when we mistreated the deceased and then proceed to torture ourselves as punishment. (However, the bereaved one may become physically exhausted by the long serious illness of the loved one and the expression of great grief is the result of a weakened body and mind.)

It is just as abnormal not to shed a tear during the ordeal of the funeral. Many patients have confessed that when their father or mother died, they felt terribly guilty because they couldn't cry. They claimed they couldn't believe it was true that their parent had died, and reacted to it with emotional numbness. It is not uncommon for these persons to suffer a *nervous breakdown* later, sometimes years afterwards, when some incident breaks down the final barrier.

In psychoanalysis we have learned the value of choosing to explode the bomb, so to speak, rather than to wait for it to go off when the patient least expects it. This is usually done by having the patient relate everything he can recall regarding his relationship to the deceased. In doing this we bring on the tears that should have been shed at the time the casket was lowered into the grave. The patient feels relieved and is able to go on to the next step in the conquest of his grief.

• *You Have to be Objective*

There is some truth in Shakespeare's statement: "Everyone can conquer grief but he who has it." But I feel that an impersonal analysis of sorrow in terms of its potential damage to our health is our wisest consolation in our hour of grief. The philosophical reflection that we all die, the rich and poor, sinner as well as saint, that Fate comes as an unwelcomed messenger of death to the door step of thousands of other homes, although it cannot bring back our departed one, tends to *make our grief more objective.*

Often a patient tells me, "I'm not too concerned about other people's misfortunes; the fact that others are worse off than I doesn't help my own problem." I do not hesitate to point out to them the selfishness of their thinking. All of us are obliged to concern ourselves with the way the rest of the world lives. We send food to starving Europe, for example, because it is our sacred duty to keep human beings, irrespective of race, color, or creed, from starving to death.

It is normal, therefore, to rationalize that grief is a universal phenomenon without necessarily becoming apathetic or stoical.

I have had to advise a mother who lost her only son in war, that her grief was an emotional injury suffered by countless other mothers whose sons had forfeited their lives that others might live in a world free of brutality. I tried to help her to think of the death of her son as the greatest sacrifice any mother could make, one that represented the greatest contribution to a better civilization. Was this merely the lip-service of psychiatry, what some might call "purchased encouragement?" Definitely not. A soul-consoling attitude is a specific first-aid rule for the control of grief.

● *Abnormal Reactions to Grief*

Abnormal reactions to grief are a sign of mental weakness. You don't have to go to the cemetery to wash a tombstone with soap and water (as I have seen done in Europe) to prove you haven't forgotten. We can make an intelligent adjustment to the death of a loved one without accusing ourselves of *forgetting* them. Actually, one *never* forgets. It is a matter of being *practical,* reminding ourselves that life must go on.

● *Grief Can Be Sublimated*

A widow may suffer a nervous breakdown. Pitied at first for her great loss, she may soon be avoided because of her constant exhibition of distress. Most of these women, unless in poor health, can find a place for themselves in the world by doing what they are best fitted for. This does not necessarily demand hard work, only confidence and determination. A good cook may set up and supervise a small tea-room; a good hand-sewer may establish a small shop for fine garments; she may be a superior baby-sitter. Whatever way she may earn her living, time and experience should improve her abilities, economic status, and emotional stability.

Sorrow can be *sublimated* by converting the emotional energy generated by grief, which would be health-consuming, into a determination to achieve a specific goal.

A friend of mine, author of a best-seller, had become morbidly despondent following the death of his sister. She had been a loyal companion to him and had encouraged him in his writing. Their parents had died many years ago. One can easily understand his feeling of emptiness, as he described it. I suggested that he get started on another book and dedicate it to the memory of his sister.

The death of my own father was a great loss to me. He symbolized everything that was fine and noble in a man. Because he emulated Lincoln in character, I had inscribed on his tombstone "With Malice Toward None and Charity For All". Just as I had advised my author-friend, I found consolation in writing a book that was dedicated to my father's memory.

There are those who adopt a life-time resolution of some kind inspired by the memory of a deceased relative or friend. Others, like war widows, console their children by telling them that their father's death symbolizes the things we fought for.

Only through sublimation of our sorrows can we emotionally withstand life's adversities.

• *Divorce: Another Mental Wound*

There are many who become hurt mentally and suffer breakdowns after a major disappointment during courtship. Others claim that their divorces represented for them the death of their love-life. Deprived of love they become disillusioned and cynical. When you allow yourself to become ill following a disappointment, it is oftentimes an indication of emotional immaturity caused by a spoiled-child complex.

If you've just returned from the divorce court, there is no reason why you should spend the rest of your life brooding about "what your marriage could have been" had circumstances been different. You could say the same thing about the whole world today, "How different it would have been if we had lost the war."

• Divorce Need Not Mean Despair

Neither should one bow his head in shame because of a previous divorce. It is never too late to try again. It is better to share life and love with another person than to clip the wings of Cupid and ground him for life.

• Too Idealistic

There are some who insist that despite their eagerness for love and happiness they simply never have come across the right person. Perhaps it is because they were *too idealistic* or they never created opportunities for themselves. I still think it is better to gamble or speculate — better to have loved and lost, than never to have loved at all.

• When You Need to See a Psychiatrist

If your impending "nervous breakdown" is associated with such conditions or symptoms as hallucinations, delusions of persecution, withdrawal from reality, acts of violence, suicidal attemps, homosexuality, drug addiction, alcoholism, sexual incompatibility, habitual criminality, sex crimes, severe anxiety states, or chronic depression, don't wait until the inevitable happens. Seek the help of a psychiatrist. Remember that an ounce of *prevention* is worth a pound of cure.

• The Easy Way Is the Best Way

Relaxed living is the *easy* way. Too many of us are *pushing* too hard. Others are *pulling* too hard. There are times when it is wiser to *glide* or just *slide*. A good swimmer conserves his energy by floating every now and then, allowing the waves to carry him closer to shore. There are so many who haven't learned the wisdom of *emotional economy*. They become too emotionally involved in everything they do, and they are consequently nervously tense and exhausted most of the time. These people are "knocking themselves out" to use a slang expression.

Would you laugh if you were to witness a heavy-weight champion accidently knock himself out while shadow-boxing during training? If you did, no one would blame you.

One day while observing my three-months old son in his crib, I noticed that he would swing his arms wildly about, hitting himself on the face. While still crying he would repeat the process. It was amusing and yet sad that I could not explain to my son that he alone was responsible for his pain. The thought occurred to me that there must be thousands of adults who are doing this very same thing — knocking themselves out by way of their self-inflicted illnesses.

It is not my intention to ridicule the person who becomes his own enemy, for psychiatrists are only too well aware of the amount of unhappiness their patients suffer because of their frustrations.

• *Negative Thinking*

Just what can you do about this self-destructive process? The first step is to recognize the fact that you are indulging in *negative thinking*. If your thought-habits are all fearful, envious, and erotic—then you will feel depressed, anxious, and disgruntled. Thinking and feeling can make a vicious cycle of cause and effect. Your own thinking habits determine whether a set-back or a tragedy of personal loss is going to cause you futile grieving or be controlled until time can heal the wound and bring you happiness again.

Negative thinking denies you your power of constructive thought. It wastes your energies and corrodes your happiness. The psychiatrist understands this from first-hand ex-

perience. He knows tragedy and disappointment and he knows
how easy it is to slip into the *destructive* way of resentment
and bitterness.

A friend of mine, a psychiatrist, lost his only son. He was
killed in a raid over enemy territory. Dr. X. had a grim battle
with despair. It was not easy to hear tales of other people's
grief, often far less than his own, and bend his sympathies and
his whole mind to their problems.

"I've been helping people with their mental problems for
over twenty-five years," he said, "now it seems to be my
turn."

A little wryly, Dr. X. added, "They say a person who packs
a parachute must be willing to use it himself to prove that
it was packed satisfactorily. The same applies to the psychiatrist. I've had to learn to let myself think of my boy as
I did at first — crashing to his death. I've learned not to let
myself brood over his childhood, and my own irrevocable loss.
He was a fighter — I must be one too. I've put my mind on
my patients, my work, on the highest goals I can achieve."

Once you have recognized the fact that your mind is a prey
to a morbid thought, the next step is to recognize it for what
it is.

• Morbid Thinking Can Become a Habit

It is when morbid thoughts become *habitual* that we are in
danger of a *breakdown*. We grow afraid of them. We try to
repress them, horrified at ourselves. Neurotics dissipate all of
their mental energy *worrying* about their *negative* thoughts.

When a patient tells me his mind is running away with him
and he is haunted by negative thoughts, he invariably says,
"I am disgusted with myself. I don't want to have these
hateful thoughts." But he does want them. Not consciously,
perhaps, but subconsciously. If there were not some deep-
seated powerful interest in these thoughts, he would not have
them. He is like the alcoholic who tells you in all sincerity,
"I really hate the stuff, but I can't leave it alone."

The patient may be quite right in saying that his negative

thinking is unwanted. Circumstances can thrust all kinds of wild ideas at us, and the human mind is capable of absolutely anything in the way of imaginings, good or evil.

The fact that he continued to let the negative mental habit grow on him, shows that he needs to find the hidden cause— the hidden desire that prompts him to go on thinking this way instead of exercising control.

Paradoxically, human beings can learn to enjoy the very things that destroy their peace of mind. Brooding has its fascinations. Fantasies of revenge or erotic pleasure can be distinctly enjoyable, once we have excused ourselves by saying we don't want them, but can't stop them. Chronic worriers enjoy feeling miserable — but only because they are in ignorance of the far greater joy that comes with mental control.

Not only the present, but the past offers temptation to negative thinking the temptation to dwell on some repressed childhood experience can result, if unchecked, in mental conflicts.

Let me emphasize once more that the mere occurrence of these thoughts is not blameworthy. *Making a habit of them is nobody's fault but your own.* For always, when these thoughts come to mind, we have a free choice of *rejection* or *acceptance.*

• *Use Your Mental Switch When You Need It*

Everyone of us has what might be called a mental switch. Nothing in the world can compel us to think a certain thought — except our own desire. You can switch off any thought that comes to you as you would a poor radio program, if you make a conscious effort.

A man with a stiff neck may read about the polio epidemic and suddenly think, "My God. Maybe I've got paralysis." At that moment he can use his mental switch. He can let the thought invade his mind, and sit and shiver amid fearful possibilities; or he can look his own thought over and say, "That's a nice gruesome idea. I could scare myself pink if I wanted to dwell on it, but I don't."

He snaps his mental switch, cuts off the negative train of thoughts, and goes on to healthier thinking. But not, remember, before he's looked the thing squarely in the face and seen it for what it is. You must deliberately investigate these mental bugaboos that come to you before you switch them off and go on, deliberately, to other matters.

Like everything else, this involves some conscious effort. But the primary effort is microscopic compared to the struggle you will have if you let bad thinking habits run away with you. If the bad thoughts have become an enslaving habit of long standing, a patient will often tell his psychiatrist, "I dare not be alone with my thoughts. They horrify me."

In this case, whenever fear of the thoughts has become ingrained, he must make himself think over those very thoughts when he least wants to. But not in a secret, shamed fashion. He must talk about them, write them down, get them entirely out of his system and into the light, just as you would lance an infection to get rid of the pus or evil matter before you can expect healing.

In this way, the man or woman who is prey to such thoughts gets them in prospective. He reduces them from fearful temptations, grief, and terrors, to mental bugaboos entirely of his own conjuring. When the fear is banished, then he can start *using his mental switch* to oust the evil germ.

• Stop Brooding

Action is the tonic that must follow unhealthy thinking. Leave yourself no time for brooding. Voltaire said, "The longer we dwell on our misfortunes, the greater is their power to hurt us."

Always there arises the wail, "But why should I be prey to such awful thoughts? Why should it happen to me to have hate thoughts, to fear diseases and death everytime I have a cold or a headache?"

The psychiatrist answers: "Why not you?" Everyone, without exception, is subject to such thoughts. You are not unique, either in your morbid thoughts, or in your good ones. All you think has been thought before and will be thought again.

Seeing yourself in perspective is a necessity if your thinking habits are going to be good ones. These habits will be the keynote to your whole personality. Like a soldier, you can alert yourself to the danger of mental misbehavior.

• *Alcohol Is no Answer*

One of the commonest present-day escapes from depressing thoughts is in the bottle. "Forget it—drink it down," shouts the happy inebriate. Tomorrow, he won't be happy, nor will he have forgotten his troubles. He'll be sick, weak, shaken, and doubly frightened by those same troubles he couldn't face the day before.

• *The Choice Is Yours*

Remember that you can literally think your way into a *nervous breakdown,* or away from one. You can think your way into chronic unhappiness or cheerful self-sufficiency. You can think your way into successful living — or suicide. The choice is *yours.*

• *Other things You Can Do to Avoid a Breakdown*

1. Guard against taking yourself too seriously.
2. Cultivate a sense of humor and learn to laugh more. Laughter tests have shown that laughter reduces muscle tone and releases the tissues, while frowning raises muscle tone and puts the body under tension and strain.
3. When things get difficult you should discuss your troubles with someone — air them out rather than keep them to yourself. Conflicts fester into mental abcesses.
4. When you feel the need of a vacation, you should take one.

5. The cultivation of a hobby is just as important as the mere acquistion of money or knowledge.
6. Keeping yourself physically fit is also essential.
7. Dispel the fears you may have developed as a result of previous misconceptions about *nervous breakdowns.*
8. If necessary read this particular chapter many times.

Session 12.

Alcohol and You

- ### *Alcohol as a Personality Illness*

Psychiatrists have learned a great deal about the person who drinks to excess. Today we know that the *alcoholic* is a *sick* individual, who suffers from a *personality-maladjustment,* who cannot face life in a mature manner.

Alcohol is a great leveler. Drinking to excess can bring a man of the higest intelligence down to the level of comatose stupidity. A man who is sober can usually rely on his intellect to keep him from getting into foolhardy situations. A man who is drunk, like the man who is mentally irrational, can become incapable of coherent thinking. He may get into trouble with the law, he may seduce his best friend's wife, or he may drive into a tree and kill himself.

- ### *Drinking May Cost You Your Life*

Exactly what excess alcohol will lead to in each individual case depends on the circumstances and the basic personality of the drinker. A woman whose husband has been unfaithful, who is disillusioned, hopeless and depressed, can drink herself into a suicidal state. Hospital and police records show that thousands of people have taken their lives under the influence of alcohol — people who would not ordinarily commit suicide on sober reflective thought.

115

• *Alcoholics Are Childish*

Excessive drinking is almost invariably indicative of some degree of instability and infantilism. Normally adult people do not need to drink themselves blind and complicate their own and everyone else's lives. The *childish* and neurotic personality is the one that takes refuge in alcohol whenever things get to be "too much for him." A man may take to alcohol because of some major disappointment or tragedy in his life that he can't face: loss of a loved one, failure in his work, or some other blow of Fate.

There are exceptional cases where the pressures of life can be so great as to drive a *normal* person to drink, but they are few.

No matter what the frustration — money reverses, disappointment in love, grief, sex tension, or whatever — *alcohol* is *never* the answer.

The element of selfishness is always present in the intoxicated person's determination to get attention at whatever cost in discomfort, embarrassment, or unhappiness to those around him.

There is one point on which there need be no confusion. Husbands and wives who are successfully and happily married do not habitually drink to excess.

• *Face Yourself*

You can be your own psychiatrist to this extent. Start with the assumption that if you crave escape in alcohol, you are a *maladjusted* man or woman. You are using a neurotic method in trying to run away from a basic problem rather than solve it. Soaking any problem in alcohol only intensifies and aggravates it, and leaves you with steadily decreasing ability to clear it up.

• *Group Psychotherapy*

I once secured permission from my hospital superintendent to organize a class to meet twice a week, made up of patients addicted to drink who were sincerely interested in ascertaining the reason for their craving and what they could do to control the habit. I used a blackboard for lecture purposes and in addition each patient was encouraged to relate the story of his life before the group, a technique devised to overcome feelings of social inferiority. Each patient was required to discuss his emotional conflicts by talking about them, somewhat like the procedure at meetings of Alcoholics Anonymous.

There were some who did not respond to this program of rehabilitation because of their resistance to treatment. But many stated upon leaving the hospital that for the first time they had developed some insight as to why they were unable to face responsibilities of life without that extra drink. I still get an occasional letter from some of the old members of the group informing me that they are still "on the wagon" after these many years.

• *Do More People Drink Today?*

Yes. The total percentage of persons who drink is steadily increasing. Sixty-four per cent of adult Americans imbibe. There are approximately 65,000,000 "social drinkers" (1 social drinker out of every 15 will wind up as an alcoholic); over 20,000,000 of them are women (one out of every 6 women becomes an alcoholic). The excessive drinkers or "problem drinkers" number around 3,000,000—a depressing figure. Of these, 750,000 are chronic or full-fledged alcoholics. 175,000 individuals lose work each day because of excessive drinking— a loss of 60,000,000 working days. The financial loss due to alcoholism is estimated to run around a billion dollars a year. Twenty-five to twenty-eight per cent of all crimes are associated with alcohol. Alcoholics have two or three times as many accidents as normal persons. They cause 10 per cent of accidents.

• *Moderate Drinking*

Alcohol is both a food and a drug. As a food it has caloric

value. In moderate quantities it serves as a tonic and *stimulant*. In larger amounts it acts as a *depressant*. Alcohol has certain useful effects. For example, alcohol moderately taken has a *sedative* action, an emotional pain-killer. It lessens anxiety and worry, relaxes the nervous system, and produces a state of well-being. Alcohol has been known to benefit persons suffering from angina pectoris. Moderate doses of alcohol dilate the coronary arteries.

Dr. Eugene M. Landis, Professor of Internal Medicine at the University of Virginia found that whiskey in amounts not exceeding two and one-half ounces per 150 pound body weight dilates the blood vessels and lasts four to five hours. Many heart specialists today feel that two highballs or cocktails, well-spaced over a 24-hour period, benefit the blood vessels of your heart.

However *excessive* drinking proves harmful to the very condition you are trying to relieve. Dr. Paul D. White, famous heart consultant, found in his clinical experience that the effect on heart and blood vessels following alcoholic intoxication is unfavorable, producing irregularities of the pulse, fast heart rate, and even heart failure in patients with certain types of heart disease.

Alcohol should not be a bugaboo to frighten ourselves with. Moderate convivial drinking has its place in life. There is no primitive tribe in this world that is not without its fermented potion of some sort.

Alcohol helps the jaded appetite and adds to the gaiety and ease of social life by releasing us from our shyness or tensions at meeting new people. It should be handled so that it breaks the ice at parties — but not so that it breaks down every reserve and leads to serious complications.

According to the National Committee on Alcoholism you are a moderate drinker *if* you drink on special occasions; *if* you do not think about your drinking; *if* you can stop when you want to; and *if* in no way does drinking present any kind of a problem.

It is not my intention to persuade anyone to stop drinking or to encourage anyone to start drinking. This chapter concerns mostly those persons who have not been able to handle alcoholic beverages well. It offers insight into compulsive drinking and gives rules to follow for problem drinkers who wish to give up alcohol.

• What Makes an Alcoholic?

There have been many articles dealing with the effects of excessive drinking on one's health, yet few writers have concentrated on the hidden or subconscious causes of alcoholism. The purpose of this chapter is to enlighten potential dipsomaniacs and social drinkers who are increasing their intake of alcohol, as well as to inform the average reader why some people feel they can't get along without alcohol.

There are various therories that explain why 3,000,000 people are driven by an inner compulsion to drink to excess.

• The Nipple-Complex Theory

Excessive indulgence in alcohol can be traced to a child-mother relationship. The alcoholic is an emotionally immature person with a nipple complex; an adult child who has never been psychologically weaned from his mother's breast —or, if bottle fed, craves a pacifier (alcohol as a nipple-substitute).

An only child is likely to be more susceptible to alcohol-addiction. There are some psychoanalysts who, following an intensive research on alcoholism have come to the conclusion that alcohol is actually a fluid-substitute for mother's milk, symbolically speaking. This will seem far fetched if you have never listened to the life stories of alcoholics. If you have, you would learn that most of them "never grew up" and have a strong oral-intake. They regress to a stage when, just like an infant, they wanted to put everything in their mouths. The alcoholic, when frustrated, wishes to return to the "nursing" period of his life. Thumb-sucking in childhood, followed by weakness for sweets and pastries, chewing-gum, cigarettes, food, and drink—all these excesses are sublimations or hangovers of this same nipple-complex present in all of us to some degree.

Those of us, however, who resort to excessive eating, drinking, smoking, and so forth, suffer from what psychiatrists call *oral erotism* (a pleasurable stimulation localized in the mouth). All alcoholics have an oral-erotic complex. It is equivalent to an adult wanting to suck a lollypop because it tastes good.

The wife of one of my patients told me that whenever her husband, who was on a strict diet because of over-weight, was emotionally upset following a quarrel with her, he would walk out of the house to the corner drug store, treat himself to a double rich malted milk, order a piece of pie a-la-mode and wind up with a bar of chocolate candy (a typical illustration of child-like behavior or oral eroticism).

Most "hard drinkers" are oversensitive and consequently are unable to withstand the frustrations of life. They are blind to the fact that they are victims of a nipple-complex and hence are unable to discipline themselves sufficiently to give up drinking. In addition, practically all of them suffer from an inferiority-complex, which they try to drown with alcohol. Dr. Edward B. Allen noted that many of the alcoholics he studied admitted that they felt inferior to their fathers and resented their inability to compete with them.

The fear of death, tension, and separation from loved ones during the war helped to make soldiers who were oral-erotics more susceptible to war-time drinking.

• The Escapism Theory

There are many normal people who dislike getting up in the morning and having to go to work. But such is life. We have to earn our bread. We can't escape our responsibilites.

Flask-carriers are forever running away from some unpleasant life-situation. They refuse to admit that through their own efforts and determination they can successfully overcome the normal problems of adult life, even though all about them they may see other people doing so.

There are various methods of escaping reality. Some take to gambling, while others become philanderers. Some take "dope", and still others prefer alcohol. The underlying motive however, is the same—to narcotize or assuage the mental pain caused by personal misfortunes. They temporarily *anesthetize* their unhappiness.

Unpaid debts, an unhappy marriage, failure in business, physical illness, fatigue and frustrations, all constitute surface-alibies for excessive drinking. The real truth is that these victims of alcoholism never developed "intestinal fortitude," the deep-seated courage to endure the common adversities of life.

• *The Psychic Suicide Theory*

Many psychiatrists are of the opinion that alcoholics are people who commit what might be termed "psychological suicide." They die a slow death, only because they are unable to recognize the true motive that unconsciously inspires their sense of defeat — their hopelessness. This of course does not apply to the moderate drinker.

Alcohol addiction becomes the compromise between the wish to live and the wish to die. It is a partial suicide — a "poisoning" of the body and mind, but usually not enough to cause death. The alcoholic lives and dies at will. He is too scared to die and too afraid to live. He lives in a third world — one in which he behaves as he likes — uninhibited.

• *The Release of Inhibitions Theory*

We all have primitive emotions for which we secretly crave an outlet. But we cannot give way to them because our sober conscience will not permit.

A man may be too inhibited to show his affection for his sweetheart. From his outward behavior you would assume that he is a "perfect gentleman." But deep inside he wishes he had the courage to put his arms around his girl and profess his love for her. Liquid stimulants loosen his tongue. Alcohol makes him the "Casanova" he wishes to be in real life. He becomes expansive and witty as well as romantic, only because he now has an excuse for his bold behavior. If he is rebuffed he can always blame it to that "one cocktail too many."

As Dr. Walter Miles stated: "Alcohol unburdens the individual of his cares and fears, relieves him of his feelings of inferiority and weakness. The inhibitions and self-criticism which ordinarily cramp his feelings tend after alcohol to be put aside."

Alcohol releases inhibitions and temporarily sets the mind free by relieving anxiety. But the alcoholic fails to realize that this is a false personality he assumes. It would be far better for him to disinhibit himself through other emotional outlets than to use alcohol as a "crutch."

Channing Brewster in an article entitled "Why I Gave Up Liquor" had this to say:

> Of course, I suffered from the malaise of the modern world-tension. No doubt alcohol removed my tension. But it acted like a spot-remover that takes the cloth with it. As I considered this favorite excuse for copious internal application of alcohol, it seemed logical to do something more basic about the tension than to pour jiggers of rum over it.[1]

• *Alcohol Releases Unhealthy Emotions*

Excessive alcohol makes some people dangerously belligerent, to the point where they pick a fight with innocent strangers. It makes men jealous, prompts them to commit crimes, encourages philandering, justifies sex offenses, and invites self-destruction by impulsive suicide. In fact, drunkenness is regarded by psychiatrists as a form of insanity.

• *Alcoholics Need to Be Re-educated*

Today statistics indicate that the alcoholic has a slightly better than 60 per cent chance of recovery.

You cannot hope to cure an alcoholic unless you succeed in

---

[1] Channing Brewster, "Why I Gave Up Liquor," *Your Life Magazine,* October 1946.

having him understand his emotional conflicts and the hidden motives responsible for his liquor habit.

The problem-drinker, however, should not be regarded as a "social outcast." He is a neurotic who needs to be under the care of a psychiatrist.

It is encouraging to note that the public's attitude is gradually changing. The stigma formerly attached to drinking is being side-tracked and our present efforts are concentrated on treatment of alcoholics as *sick* people.

Experience has taught the psychiatrist that if he cures his patient of his *personality-conflicts,* the symptom (excessive craving for alcohol) subsequently disappears.

• *25 Commandments*

The late Dr. Robert Seliger, instructor in neurology and psychiatry at Johns Hopkins University, made an extensive study of alcoholism. He formulated the following set of rules. The person who *drinks to excess* is bound to benefit by them. Any intelligent person with average common sense can cure himself of alcoholism if he is *willing* to develop, with the aid of a psychiatrist if necessary, the self-discipline and maturity needed to obey Seliger's 25 commandments.

1. Face squarely the fact that you can't control your drinking and therefore never will be able to control your drinking.
2. Realize what alcohol does for you and that the problem for you is not merely one of dissipation but of a dangerous psychopathological reaction to what is for you a pernicious drug.
3. Understand that without abstinence you never can have a contented and efficient life.
4. Be absolutely sincere in wanting to stop drinking.
5. Realize that giving up alcohol is your problem and that while you need help in giving it up, no one but yourself can make you stop drinking.
6. Be convinced that any reasonably intelligent and sincere person who is willing to make a sus-

tained effort over a sufficient period of time
can learn to live without alcohol.

7. Accept the fact that it takes a year at least for
an alcoholic to reorganize his life.

8. Work with whole-hearted cooperation with the
psychiatrist who is trying to help you.

9. Realize that only by understanding the motive
behind your drinking can you eliminate the
cause.

10. Follow carefully a daily, self-imposed schedule
which, conscientiously carried out, aids in improving health, building a disciplined personality, developing new habits for old and bringing out a new rhythm of living.

11. Realize that the care of your physical health
is an important part of your rehabilitation.

12. Learn the importance of eating — since the
best preventive of that tired, jittery feeling
which so often leads to taking a drink is food —
and carry with you at all times chocolate bars
or other candy to pep you up when you are low
in spirits and strength.

13. Avoid needless hurry and fatigue.

14. Avoid emotional disturbances.

15. Be especially on guard during periods of change
in your life involving some emotional or nervous
fatigue.

16. Learn to relax naturally, mentally and physically, without the use of the narcotizing alcohol.

17. Learn to be controlled by your judgment instead
of by your emotions.

18. Don't daydream about past drinking.

19. Avoid the small glass of wine — i.e., the apparently harmless lapse — with even more determination than the obvious slug of gin.

20. Don't fool yourself that you can drink beer.

21. Understand that alcoholic ancestry is an excuse,
not a reason for abnormal drinking.

22. Don't be discouraged by any feeling of discontent during the early stages of sobriety, but

turn this feeling into an incentive to action
which will satisfy legitimately your desire for
self-expression.

23. Disregard the dumb advice and often dumber
questions of relatives and friends, without becoming emotionally disturbed.

24. Realize that people seeking help for abnormal
drinking are usually above average in intellectual endowment and that while drinking
means failure, abstinence is likely to mean marked success.

25. Don't feel that any of these commandments are
in any way inconsequential, or secondary to
business, play or whatnot; and conscientiously
observe every one of them, day in and day out.

Session 13.

~~~~~~

You Can Avoid
an Unhappy Marriage

● *Selecting a Mate*

There are too many disillusioned husbands and broken-hearted wives who lead empty lives because of their error in judgment during courtship.

Just as farmers can generally predict bad weather from a glance at the horizon, psychiatrists have learned to recognize what inevitably will turn out to be an unfortunate marriage.

As I look back, trying to recall cases of couples who had tried in vain to patch up an unhappy marriage, I arrive at the conclusion that the fault usually lies with one or both of them having exercised bad judgment in selecting a mate.

Incidently, poor judgment is not limited to the uneducated. Many college graduates prove to be victims of impulsive decisions and consummate bad marriages.

Patients have asked me, "Is there any way that one can tell whether or not marrying a certain person will turn out to be a good or bad risk?" The answer is "Yes" — by learning to recognize during courtship those personality-traits and weaknesses that invariably lead to future unhappiness.

126

• Danger Signals

In courtship you are in the same position as the pilot of a small cabin cruiser. You must acquaint yourself with elementary laws of navigation, know when a storm is approaching, be able to sight shallow waters, and, most important of all, be able to prevent your boat from running on the rocks. You must be able, in other words, to recognize definite danger signals that should warn you of the threatening reefs of an unhappy marriage.

• Compulsive Drinking

The men or women who drink to excess, as previously pointed out, suffer from a serious *personality-maladjustment*. They constitute a *bad* risk. The fact that a man is able to earn a good living despite his drinking doesn't make him eligible for marriage. If the woman suspects that he is more than a "social drinker," she saves herself a lifetime of grief by putting thumbs down on the proposal. It's not worth the gamble. Inebriates belong to the unmarriageable group. They tend to make alcoholics of their wives. It is best to be cautious when a suitor promises to give up drinking after the wedding ceremony. Many women flatter themselves by thinking that they have reformed a "Lost Week-End" lover and that his case is an exception to the rule, where a weakness for alcohol is concerned. All too soon after the honeymoon, the husband slips back into his drinking habits.

There is nothing so intolerable as to have an alcoholic husband or wife on your hands. Drinking has wrecked many a marriage. You can either play safe by marrying a nondrinker or someone who is no more than a social drinker, or risk the consequences if your guess was wrong about his promise to give up drinking.

• Unfaithfulness

Allied with drinking is the next danger-signal — *philandering*. The woman who has one highball too many very often becomes susceptible to adultery. That goes for men also, and this is another reason why alcoholics make a poor risk for a happy marriage. Alcohol has a tendency to destroy our inhibitions, to hypnotize our conscience, and to make it easy to forget our marriage vows.

Drinking to excess encourages men to become woman-chasers. It is worse with women who philander, because of the possibility of physical complications.

Instinctively we all have polygamous tendencies. To live monogamously is simply a matter of social ethics and self-discipline, foregoing temptations. Today, we don't judge a first offender by the particular crime he has committed. We take into careful consideration the motive that prompted him to violate a certain law. Likewise, each case of unfaithfulness during courtship must be evaluated according to the particular circumstances involved.

A woman who continually talks about other men while being courted generally makes a flirtatious wife. Even though she claims that her affair with Jack or Bill did not involve any physical intimacy, it does not make her flirting excusable.

If you feel your engaged partner has tendencies toward being unfaithful, judging from his or her past record, it would be best to give it serious thought before you make that final commitment, "I do".

• *Emotional Immaturity*

Neurotics have one thing in common—*emotional immaturity*. It explains why the child-like behavior of a wife or a husband taxes the nerves of the other partner beyond endurance. As Dr. Rudolf Von Ruban has said: "Neurotics are like children. They should not marry until the influences that block their specific radiations have been overcome. Every marriage in which either partner is immature is a risk".

Larry had just been offered an excellent position in California and consequently decided to propose to his girl, Dorothy, whom he had known for a long time. When he spoke to her of his intentions to settle in the West, Dorothy protested that she could never live away from her parents. She insisted that he get a position in New York City and suggested that they share her parents' home. She told of her devotion to her folks and how much they meant to her.

Emotionally immature persons of this kind are the first to run home to "mama" and "papa" when marital friction develops. The normal girl should be able to detach herself from her family and be willing to accept a new future in her husband's chosen environment. Living close to one's parents invites in-law complications, a serious threat to marital happiness.

There are equally as many men who cannot make up their minds whether to marry and break away from home or remain single, preferring mother's home-cooking and companionship. Grown-ups who are unable to sever unhealthy family ties are not quite ready for marriage.

If they do marry, trouble is just around the corner. Usually such persons manifest extreme possessiveness and become jealous at the first sign of any displacement of affection.

• *Jealousy*

There are men who become jealous whenever their girl friend dances with the same man twice, falsely accuse her of being too friendly, and question her about every place she goes. This kind of jealousy is a hangover from a childhood instinct of *over-possessiveness*. It is a sign of one's own feelings of inferiority.

Morbid jealousy goes far beyond the normal. It is normal jealousy curdled into a sickness of the mind.

Men and women who are unreasonably jealous generally suffer either from a feeling of insecurity, or they feel guilty because of their conscious or unconscious desire to commit adultery.

I'm speaking, of course, of unjustified jealousy. One usually finds jealousy existing in a man who is courting an exceptionally attractive woman and, vice versa, in a girl whose handsome boy friend is admired by all the ladies.

I have also found from experience that wives who consult me because of their husband's abnormal jealousy describe the husband as being sexually inadequate (another warning for those who are in love with victims of a jealousy-complex).

It is a serious misconception to conclude that jealousy is a sign of true love. On the contrary, it may indicate that the person wishes to marry from a neurotic motive — to over-possess the other person for physical gratification only, to *desire* love instead of *giving* it.

● Sex Complexes

According to recent statistics, the majority of divorces are caused by sexual incompatibility. I didn't realize how true this was until I began listening to the many confessions of frustrated husbands and wives. Like listening to the same victrola record. I am repeatedly asked: "Since one's parents and religion as well as society condemn premarital intimacies, how then can you be sure that the person you marry will be the right choice from the standpoint of sexual compatibility?"

The same way that a psychiatrist determines whether or not his patient will actually commit suicide, is the answer. There is no certainty. The psychiatrist can only arrive at his conclusions by getting the patient to say enough to finally betray himself. In talking with someone about sex, you can soon learn if he harbors normal or neurotic attitudes toward that which is essential to his happiness in marriage.

No one is adequately prepared for marriage unless he possesses a reasonable amount of sex education. I insist that my unmarried patients read at least two or three authoritative books on the subject. It is because of premarital sexual ignorance that we find women married to impotent men and suffering nervous breakdowns as a consequence; or men married to frigid women with resultant excuses for extramarital relations.

Marriage is no solution to one's sexual conflicts. Those who suspect they are sexually inadequate should not marry until they have been cured of their particular sexual disorders.

The girl who speaks of sex as something sordid, who minimizes the role that sex harmony plays in marriage is potentially a bad matrimonial risk. Likewise, a man who is abnormally inhibited and behaves as though he were courting his sister often turns out to be a clumsy lover. His inadequacy becomes the source of much grief.

A patient told me she was afraid to marry a certain young man who had proposed because she had been going with him for three years and he behaved so much like a perfect gentleman (never having made an attempt to kiss her) that she began to wonder if he knew the "facts of life."

It is alarming to discover after marriage that your husband or wife prefers to sleep in a separate bedroom, particularly when you realize that sexual incompatibility can lead to neurotic illness.

• Chronic Unhappiness

Unhappy people as a rule make bad marriage partners. They complain a lot, are inclined to be health-conscious and are constantly dissatisfied. The most predominant characteristic is their *chronic unhappiness*.

It is best to think twice about walking to the altar with a woman or man who becomes frequently depressed, who enjoys criticizing everyone and everything, who suffers from exaggerated ailments, and who frequently displays an ugly disposition by becoming abusive, angry, and argumentative. You assume a heavy liability when you risk marriage to a person of this type.

• Teen-Age Marriages Are Risky

In my experience the majority of men and women who married under the age of 21 regretted the marriage. Unfortunately, the parents themselves sometimes encourage these early marriages. Such parents labor under the misapprehension that early marriage will have a maturing and stabilizing effect on the difficult teen-ager. I have always encountered parents who were anxious to marry off their children, in order to relieve themselves of the responsibility for any delinquent behavior on the part of the son or daughter. Teen-age marriages are based on impulsive decisions. The odds are heavily against

them. Usually both boy and girl are emotionally immature
and spoiled. They want what they want when they want it,
irrespective of whether or not it will end in disaster.

• *Impulsive Marriages Are Sometimes Caused by Sex-Hunger*

The basic trouble with the teen-age marriage is that it is
based on *selfishness* and on a faulty attitude toward sex. The
teen-agers who are determined to marry at all costs turn a
deaf ear to the advice of parents. Premature sexual stimulation gives them the idea of getting more sex through immediate marriage. They experience sex hunger, like food hunger,
and are not satisfied with one piece of pie; they want the
whole pie. Then, feeling sick, they rush home to their parents
for help like the children they are.

• *Disadvantages of Early Marriages*

The boy is, in my estimation, more to blame than the girl.
The teen-age boy who has no permanent job and hasn't even
finished his education, believes in magic. He thinks love-
making can satisfy all his wife's needs. She may also think
so, until reality catches up with them. Neither of them can
assume the responsibilities necessary for a happy marriage.
When marriage comes early, usually motherhood comes early,
and complications set in. Financial hardships produce mutual
irritability, then sexual coldness. Infidelity and divorce are
the unhappy ending of the idyl.

There are a few exceptions, case in which teen-age marriages do work out. These are rare. Even when the marriage
does work out, both husband and wife have the feeling in
later years that they robbed themselves of an opportunity to
experience adult years on their own.

The teen-agers who marry commit themselves before they
have had a chance to look around, to compare and select.
Many of them cheat after marriage because they resent having
missed single life and try to make up for what they have
missed.

I have found, too, that when the teen-agers are willing

to give up their education in order to marry they are likely to quit their marriage in later years. Then they find themselves with an incomplete education and a broken marriage.

• *Irene Mistook Sex for Love*

The case of Irene and her high-school sweetheart, Martin, is typical of the impulsive teen-age marriage and its disastrous consequences.

Irene was the belle of her high school group. She had been voted the prettiest girl in her grade. She was spoiled and selfish not simply because of her looks, but because her father had doted on her from babyhood. Both her parents were proud of her and devoted to her. They had mapped out a glowing future for her which was to include a college education at one of the best schools in the country.

Neither had given her any sex education at all.

Irene met a boy in school who was apparently a perfect match for her. He was handsome, smooth, and poised. At seventeen he had been physically intimate with many girls, and it was not hard for him to charm the ignorant fifteen-year old girl into giving herself to him.

She mistook it all for real love and was doubly convinced when he insisted that they marry. She had no way of knowing that it was not love on his part but a jealous desire to keep his pretty girl as an exclusive possession. They married secretly and each lived at home with the family.

• *The Beginning of Complications*

Irene began failing in all her studies, and never finished high school. Martin had dropped out of school altogether, but hadn't bothered to look for a job. He made his young wife pregnant—and at that point they told the parents about the marriage.

Irene's parents were so bitterly disappointed and shocked that they refused to help at all. They would have nothing to do with Martin. His parents also refused to help. He had to take a poorly paid job, and the young couple lived in a wretched back room.

Irene frightened by her pregnancy and grieved over her parents' refusal to help, grew more and more despondent. In her depressed state, she did not appeal to Martin any more. He spent his evenings in taverns, and was soon being unfaithful to her.

Irene became suicidal and told her parents she intended to kill herself. That frightened them into helping her. They sent her to me. I had Martin come to my office to find out what hope there was of salvaging the marriage.

Martin made matters quite clear. He assured me that Irene was to blame for the whole situation. "She didn't have to marry me," he said.

• Divorce Was Inevitable

The one interview with him was sufficient. Martin went his way. Irene obtained a divorce and had her baby—a baby having a baby was what it amounted to. She considered the baby as a child does a doll. She later told me that her love for the baby, her dread of taking another life with her own during her pregnancy, was all that had kept her from killing herself.

Irene was robbed of her youthful, carefree years, of the education and the bright promise her parents had wanted for her. They had thought it sufficient, during her high school romance, to warn her of the inadvisability of too early a marriage. They hadn't warned her at all of the sexual pressures from within and from without, during those crucial years. They hadn't warned her to be on guard against her own adolescent sex hunger, and to be on guard against the blind impulses of the boys she would meet who would make them both victims of ignorance and lack of control.

• Hindsight

Irene, on her last visit to me, said what hundreds of girls just like her have said: "If I had only known then what I do now, I'd never have married so young under any circumstances, no matter how promising it looked."

Premature marriages among adolescents are like unripened fruit. The outcome is indigestion and suffering. The mind, like the fruit, must ripen.

The heart and mind must be regarded as a partnership. In any successful partnership, as in business, it is illegal to transact anything without the assent of both partners. Heart and mind must agree on a decision to marry. This safeguards both the emotional and the practical aspects of married happiness. It saves the boy or girl from rushing into a marriage based on sexual satisfaction only. It also saves the boy or girl from a loveless marriage, based solely on money or social position. Both types are foredoomed to failure.

• *When in Doubt*

If you are in doubt about yourself or the other person, consult a marriage counselor. At least he will see to it that your *heart* doesn't rule your *mind*. Perhaps some day all engaged couples, instead of the present-day few, will be able to go to a marriage clinic where they can determine if they are properly suited to each other. It will mean fewer divorces and fewer neurotic children.

When Your Marriage Is at the Crossroads

• *Less Need for Divorces*

Thirty-four out of every 100 marriages wind up in pathetic failure (400,000 divorces a year). About 32 million husbands and wives now living together in the United States will be divorced. Our divorce rates are the highest in the world. One authority claims that "no more than half of American families are happy and well-adjusted to the degree that the average person expects when he marries."

There are entirely too many impulsive marriages resulting in thousands of equally impulsive divorces. The frequency of indiscriminate divorces is very demoralizing to the whole of modern society. If all of us assumed the responsibility of encouraging married persons to look within themselves for the cause of their unhappiness and, if necessary, to seek professional advice and help, there would be less need for dissolving the marriage.

• Sick *Marriages Are Caused by* Sick *Personalities*

Many divorces can be *prevented* provided the partners in marriage are able to face their difficulties *realistically* and are willing to make necessary concessions. Above all they must be willing to accept their own responsibility for their marital discord. An unhappy marriage is seldom a one-sided affair. It is two people getting on each other's nerves and both partners having a vital need for guidance and awakening if the marriage is to be saved.

While on the surface the outlook for happy marriages appears gloomy, Dr. David R. Mace and Evan McCleod Wylie, in an article entitled "Your Marriage Today" (*Woman's Home Companion*, April 1956) have found that "despite the many important new perils to marriage, it is fair to say that our best marriages today have never been surpassed in any other period in American history. And that with proper understanding of the relatively new difficulties they face and full use of the new knowledge at their disposal, more married couples should be able to reach these peaks of happiness and fulfillment than ever before."

• *The Unhappily Married*

Persons who find themselves in an unhappy marriage do one of several things:

1. They make martyrs of themselves, suffer in their unhappiness, and do nothing to improve a situation that becomes more and more intolerable. Something usually happens. The wife or husband has a nervous breakdown or they go to their family physician with various health-complaints not knowing that these ailments are disguised expressions of their marital unhappiness.

2. They keep their marriage intact but live in separate worlds. Their physical relations become infrequent. The husband finds an outlet for his domestic frustrations through philandering, which he conceals, or the wife tries to justify her infidelity on the basis that she is not ap-

preciated and loved by her husband. Here again we can expect complications. There are enough newspaper accounts of crimes committed because of jealousy, suicides, and alienation of affection suits to prove this.

3. They seek a divorce only to discover years later that a divorce was not the answer to their problem. They more than likely encounter unhappiness in a subsequent marriage because they are blind to the fact that the root-cause of their difficulty lies within themselves.

4. They seek the help of a psychiatrist or marriage counselor for various reasons. Some are advised to do so by their physician, clergyman, or friend. Others have learned that many marriages can be saved if the causes responsible for the incompatibility are eliminated. With the honest cooperation of both husband and wife, the results are generally favorable.

• *Why Marriages Fail*

The question is often asked: "Why is it that so many marriages end in divorce?" Dr. Edmund Berger, author of *Unhappy Marriage and Divorce* [1] shows that "the roots of marital failure reach far back into the childhood of the marriage partners, when a pattern of neurotic behavior was unconsciously established and that this pattern has, in turn, led to a neurotic choice of marriage partners."

• *Many Marry for Reasons Other Than Love*

A patient recently admitted to me that the only reason she married her husband, whom she didn't love, was to get away from her unhappy parents. She had been exposed to constant quarreling at home and felt she had to escape.

Some marry for money, while others accept marriage because of its convenience. Then there are marriages that are maneuvered by parents without regard to whether or not the two people love each other. Fortunately these are in the minority today.

---

[1] Dr. Edmund Bergler, *Unhappy Marriage and Divorce*. New York: International Universities Press, Inc., 1949.

• Illness Can Be Responsible for Marital Difficulties

A couple sought advice because of their frequent personality clashes. Mrs. B. complained that her husband didn't love her as much as he formerly did. She based this on the fact that he was spending more time at the club, paid less attention to the children, and seldom took her out to dinner or to a social function. Mr. B. claimed he had noticed a definite change in his wife—that she was irritable, complained constantly about not feeling well, criticized everything he did, and accused him of no longer loving her, keeping him awake at night with conversation of this kind. He had her examined by several doctors and was told she was going through the menopause and that he had to expect a certain amount of change in her personality.

Actually, it was discovered that she was suffering from a condition known as "involutional melancholia." Women in their middle years sometimes develop this mental condition, which is characterized by emotional instability, frequent crying spells, undue fatigue, dissatisfaction with everything, spells of depression, and a feeling that everything is hopeless, that they are ill and will never get well, and that they have lost their husband's love. These unhappy symptoms are brought on by feelings of self-pity and a loss of confidence in themselves, by frustration in their relationship to their husband, and by their inability to adjust well to their advancing years and the glandular changes that come with them.

• The Male Menopause

Men also go through an equivalent of the female menopause. They do not feel quite the same as they used to. Some become grumpy, serious-minded and complain of numerous ailments. Unable to recognize the source of their trouble, they get on the nerves of the other person.

• The Impossible Marriages

The greatest number of divorces, however, are caused by the impossible marriages. The husband and wife are not only mismated, victims of a maladjusted love-life, but they refuse to make any effort to remedy a situation that continues to remain intolerable. The alcoholic, homosexual, Don Juan, or wife-beating husband, for example, who rejects any kind of treatment comes under this classification. There are thousands of wives who suffer mental breakdowns because they are victims of physical and mental cruelty at the hands of sadistic husbands.

• Divorce-Producing Complications

Marriages fail for many reasons. Jealousy, infidelity, in-law complications, interfaith conflicts, and sexual incompatibility very often lead to the divorce court. Sex difficulties in marriage, however, will be discussed in a separate chapter. Jealousy and infidelity are two of the most common complications, and consequently merit further discussion.

• Jealousy

The tragedy among human lives caused by jealousy cannot be estimated. Almost daily we read in the newspapers about someone who has been shot or stabbed because of being involved in a love-triangle.

While jealousy-crimes have occurred from the beginning of time, we find that after every war the divorce rate steps up. Many of these broken marriages are due to infidelity, real or suspected.

Numerous couples have been interviewed who were on the verge of leaving for Reno, because the wife confessed she had gone to a movie or a dance with some friend while her husband was overseas; or the husband decided to supplement his battle experiences with an account of the girl in London or Australia who was a perfect companion on a sight-seeing tour. The incident was harmless, but a suspicious jealousy was aroused that finally led to a furious quarrel.

The question invariably arises: "Is jealousy ever justified when true love exists?" Most persons harbor the misconception that jealousy is definitely a weakness or shortcoming in a person's character, that it is a disease of the soul, and consequently refer to it in a derogatory manner.

No one denies that jealousy based on false suspicions can be as fatal to a happy marriage as cancer can be to some vital organ of the body. But there are times when it is normal for a husband or wife to be jealous.

• *Jealousy as a Protective Emotion*

There are few of us who have not at one time or another experienced jealousy-distress. Like fear, jealousy is a protective emotion. It is the whistle on the tea kettle that warns us when a love-frustration reaches the boiling temperature. It is the quantity and quality of this jealousy that we express in a given situation that determines whether or not it is normal or abnormal. Just as a person may be justified in being afraid under certain circumstances, one can become normally jealous when his suspicions are not the product of his morbid imagination but are based on facts.

• *Two Kinds of Jealousy*

(1) *Love-protection jealousy* (not divorce-producing); (2) *Love-adulterated jealousy* (capable of dissolving marriages).

A man who suspected his wife of an infidelity came to me and told me he had tried every means he could to extract a confession from her, but she insisted she was innocent. He wanted me to administer truth serum to her, then to report to him all the details of the infidelity he was sure she would confess.

The husband had to be told that no psychiatrist would do this type of detective work. The psychiatrist does not "extract" confessions. He does not break down patients for the purpose of giving the husband or wife grounds for divorce— or for lifelong recrimination. I told him that whatever his wife revealed would be kept confidential. It would be used only to help both of them rehabilitate their marriage. The husband walked out of my office in a rage.

This man's attitude and behavior showed him to be the one who needed the treatment. He was suffering from a typical manifestation of *abnormal jealousy*. He was not interested in restoring good relations in his marriage, but in satisfying his curiosity and his obsession for revenge.

• *Confessions of Unfaithfulness*

From many experiences, I have found that when a husband gets a confession of infidelity from his wife, his jealousy, althought justified, turns into a sickening, morbid type. It is a different emotion from the first normal anger. It feeds on its own misery.

He uses his wife's confession to torture himself and her. He questions her over and over about it. He wants to know all the details of the infidelity, even to the physical technique.

• *Projection of the Husband's Guilt*

Several months ago a middle-aged woman who had lost all appetite for food and complained of an inability to sleep, stated that her husband aged 55, was persecuting her with accusations of infidelity. It was discovered that her husband had been philandering and was evidently projecting his own guilt on to his wife, accusing her in order to relieve his own tormented conscience. This is quite common. This case illustrates by contrast the kind of jealousy that is considered abnormal.

Many husbands who accuse their wives of infidelity without having sufficient grounds for their suspicions betray in this way their own philandering guilt or their fears of losing their sexual potency.

• *A Sense of Fair Play*

In marriage there must be a sense of fair play. No husband should make his wife feel anchored down as though she had a ball-and-chain around her ankle, but, nevertheless, he should make her realize that it is her duty to forfeit certain liberties if she wishes to prevent marriage-complications. The same holds true for husbands.

• *Why Invite Trouble?*

Persons who, without motive, engage in friendly letter-writing with former rival sweethearts provoke the kind of jealousy that is justified. There are thousands of divorces that have resulted from a husband or wife picking up a letter that haunted their imagination. It is normal to be jealous when the other partner writes or receives a letter that is more than friendly. Those who are indiscreet about expressing their sentiments in letter-writing are inviting trouble.

Regarding our conduct at a social affair, one can be gay and happy without kissing or "pawing" everyone's wife or husband. Such behavior is never condoned. It is a breach of etiquette; a respectable host or hostess expects guests not to offend one another and not to act in a common or vulgar manner.

A patient recently related how at a party her husband, whose handsomeness was accentuated by his Navy uniform, cornered an attractive Wave and openly resorted to "heavy petting" after having had too much to drink. The wife herself had been approached by a good-looking married man but she discouraged him, for she did not think that two wrongs made a right. Her friends began teasing her about her husband's brazen love-making until she lost control, walked over to her husband and informed him that they were leaving. He became angry, and this led to a free-for-all duel of words. He then began to twist her arm, explaining that it was about time she got over being insanely jealous. His wife found it necessary to bite him to make him stop injuring her arm and shouted to everyone's amusement that he was making a fool of himself.

The husband agreed later that his behavior at the party was uncalled for and that he wouldn't have liked it if the tables had been turned.

We are all normally sensitive. In marriage, it is impossible to engage in flirtation, even if it seems innocent, without hurting someone. It is normal for our partner to be jealous when we deliberately break the rules of the game. However when two people are intelligently considerate of each other's feelings, there is never a jealousy-problem.

• *Don't Deliberately Try to Make Him Jealous*

Some wives, because they feel neglected in marriage, think if they can make their husbands jealous, they can rekindle the fire of love between them. Such strategy often results in tragic consequences, just as it does in courtship. Many a girl has lost a potential husband because she spent the evening recounting the attractions of a rival suitor.

• *Forgiving Means Forgetting*

Each jealousy-problem requires individual consideration. There are numerous cases of justified jealousy among veterans who returned home and discovered wartime infidelity of their wives. In some instances the isolated episode of unfaithfulness may be considered an "accident," and hence the wife should be forgiven. But forgiving means forgetting. To remind the other person of her past sexual transgressions or to torture yourself with revenge-fantasies is definitely a symptom of a morbid-jealousy complex. Infidelity following forgiveness is altogether a different matter and requires a more drastic solution.

When Judge Kovachy of Cleveland, who heard 3,500 divorce cases in six months, was interviewed by the press, he stated that the nation's divorce problems had become serious and that too many veterans immediately sought a divorce because their wife went to a picture show or danced with someone of the opposite sex, and too many wives consulted a divorce lawyer because a homesick soldier-husband wrote letters to old girl friends from their lonely foxholes. He advocated a little *forgiving* and *forgetting* to prevent these broken marriages.

• Infidelity

Infidelity is a major cause of the ever-increasing divorce rate.

According to Kinsey, "About half of all the married males have intercourse with women other than their wives at some time while they are married."

Many marriage casualties arrive at the conclusion that divorce is the only answer to their problem. However, as long as the underlying causes of infidelity are not uncovered, these people, when they get their divorce and remarry, often find themselves in the same situation because of never having resolved those inner conflicts that caused the original infidelity.

Infidelity in many instances is a symptom-expression of some basic underlying neurosis. To understand it in terms of its realistic implications, moral prejudices must be held in abeyance. Each case of unfaithfulness must be evaluated in accordance with the particular set of physical or emotional circumstances in which it arose.

Infidelity is a problem that needs far more widespread understanding than it has today. Men and women should know what preventive steps they can take when infidelity threatens to break up their marriage. They need to be prepared for it when it comes.

Most people feel that it won't happen in their marriage, but it can happen to anyone, the normal as well as the neurotic, the happily married as well as the unhappy. A good swimmer can drown. We are all potentially susceptible to giving expression to our polygamous inclinations.

Few people can answer yes to the question: "Would I be levelheaded and do the right thing about it, if my married partner were unfaithful?" When it does happen, those involved are too close to it, too blinded by emotion to act reasonably. Men and women both become *hysterical*.

• Consequences of Infidelity

Crimes of passion are a frequent result of infidelity. Suicides occur when people have not been given any perspective on the problem. They feel they are suffering the worst thing that could ever happen to them, and their lives are ruined. Murder of the "other man" is a common occurence. Sometimes both suicide and murder result when a triangle situation has reached the explosive point.

Your newspaper carries such violent examples as this one: A wife and mother left her husband in a temporary separation. During the separation, she embarked on a love affair with another man. With the typical instability of the love affair, this one ended in a quarrel. The woman told her lover that she was going to return to her husband. In a fit of jealous rage he shot and killed her, then killed himself, all in the presence of her two small children.

Married couples who ignore the possibility of infidelity are like plane pilots who know how to manage their plane only in calm weather. When storms come up they are lost. The lives of the passengers depends on the pilot. Children are passengers in marriage. They depend on the judgment of their parents. When the adults lose control, the children are the innocent victims of the wreck.

• Physical Infidelity

Almost every case of infidelity involves sexual intimacy. There are very few *platonic* infidelities in which a husband or wife trysts clandestinely for the sake of friendship only. Because infidelity involves a problem in sex behavior, it comes or should come within the psychiatrist's field. Unfortunately most cases of infidelity are settled by the husband or wife in a blind rage, or by lawyers in the divorce court, where infidelity plays such a leading role.

• The Bad Marriage

A bad marriage is generally the result of mismating. The husband and wife were either emotionally unsuited for each other, being opposite personality-types, or they were unfit for good marriages by reason of psychological immaturity or premarital neurotic complexes. Having been conditioned by an early neurotic home environment and unhappy childhood, these individuals are incapable of developing a normal love relationship toward the opposite sex. As a result, it may be assumed that the marriage was neurotically motivated.

In many years of listening to the domestic difficulties of several hundred couples, I have had an opportunity to observe the tragic mistakes made by those patients who impulsively chose divorce instead of adjustment, and others who profited by attempting to remedy the cause of their incompatibility.

• *A Wife in Name Only*

Joan was an only child who had always had her own way. She grew up spoiled and selfish. Jim, her husband, was a passive, weak, obsequious type, whereas Joan was aggressive, dominating, and masculine. She had a father-complex and was incapable of accepting the wife-role in marriage. The husband complained that she was not willing to fulfill her physical obligations. She regarded herself as his wife in name only and wished to do as she pleased to the extent that she became unfaithful during a vacation trip.

It was suggested that they both submit to psychoanalysis with the hope of saving the marriage. She refused, stating that there was nothing wrong with her, that her husband was a clumsy lover and consequently a separation was the only answer. She obtained a Reno divorce.

In the meantime her husband was psychoanalyzed, became aware of his shortcomings, corrected them and launched out on a new life for himself. Fate was kind to him. He met the right type of girl this time, having exercised better judgment in the selection of a mate, and married her. He is now completely happy. Joan on the other hand, fared badly after the divorce.

Letters she sent to him made it clear that she had found the divorce a sad mistake. Until she finds herself, through self-analysis or professional guidance, she will continue to make some other husband unhappy.

• How Can a Bad Marriage be Saved?

A bad marriage can be saved in one of two ways:

1. Through a mutual plan of self-analysis, development of new insight, and application of necessary discipline.
2. Through the help of a psychiatrist or marriage counsellor if the incompatibility involves deep-seated conflicts, or if the personal efforts of the couple toward saving the marriage has failed.

Many couples fear taking their troubles to a psychiatrist or psychoanalyst, thinking they will be told that a divorce is their only salvation. Quite the contrary. The physician does everything possible to bring a husband and wife into a more harmonious relationship.

Perhaps by passing on to you a method of approach used in handling the marital difficulties of a typical couple who are on the verge of going their separate ways, you may acquire a similar technique that will prove successful in solving your own marriage problem without having to resort to outside help.

• It Requires Cooperation

The *first step* is to determine according to the description of the bad and impossible marriages just where yours stands. If it's a bad marriage and you are both willing to cooperate in changing the situation, start by not expecting too much of the other person. Remember that domestic compatibility is something you work for and not something fictitious you read about in a love novel. You don't have to strive for perfection, which incidentally is a neurosis in itself.

• To Be Happy Is to Be Human

Persons who insist on doing everything in a precise way are obnoxious.

I'm reminded of a patient who tries so hard to improve her husband's diction, is so eager to correct other people's faults, and keeps her child under such perfect control that she alienates husband, friends, and child. You must make allowances for the faults of others.

You cannot expect your partner in marriage to cater to all your whims, to think as you do, to fulfill all your demands, some of which may be unreasonable. This kind of possessiveness makes for a bad marriage. Every husband and wife is entitled to hold on to a certain amount of their premarital individuality. Couples are sometimes unhappy because the wife expects the husband to keep a halo constantly over his head or the husband wants his wife to sprout a pair of angel's wings. You must allow for what may be called "normal incompatibility."

• Look Within Yourself

The *next step* is to analyze yourself. Make a good job of it. Ask yourself these questions. "What was the nature of the relationship that existed between my mother and father? Did they love each other? If my parents are divorced, what effect did a broken home have on me? Did I come from a neurotic family? What was my early home environment like?"

Such information may enable you to discover the source of your marital unhappiness — the neurotic influences that have carried over into married life.

In looking over my records I discovered that often a wife who was anxious to get a divorce came from divorced parents. The same is true for husbands who blamed their wives for the failure of the marriage. It is more than a coincidence that persons who come from broken homes are more susceptible to marital unhappiness. Hence, it is important in taking an inventory of yourself to make sure that the unhappiness of your parents or the frustrations suffered in your early childhood do not unconsciously influence your present attitudes toward love, sex, and marriage.

• The Answer May Give You a Valuable Clue

Ask yourself, "What sort of person was I before I married?

Was I unhappy? Why did I marry? Have I been an asset or a liability to my partner in marriage? Do people like me? What personality defects do I possess? Are my attitudes toward sex quite normal?" If you answer these questions honestly you may discover the reason for much of your difficulty.

• *Overhaul Yourself*

Despite what the other person is like, you must work on yourself. In three to six months, with self-acquired insight, self-discipline, and determination you can become a better person. *The one sure way of changing your husband or wife is to change yourself.* Square it with your conscience that you have held up your half of the bargain—that you have made every possible effort to make your marriage partner happy. *Self-analysis* and *self-improvement* are the *first steps* in the solution of a bad marriage.

If you feel you have developed sufficient insight into your own emotional make-up, then you should be able to appreciate those factors in your husband or wife's past life that account for the present incompatibility. Try to discuss your conclusions with your mate in a diplomatic manner, without assuming an air of superiority or belittlement.

You'll become more tolerant when you evaluate your partner's behavior in terms of motivations traced back to the family background and childhood. The trouble with most unhappy couples lies in the fact they are blind to their own personality-shortcomings and project onto the other person their premarital unhappiness. All unpleasant conversation should be eliminated if you desire to achieve happiness in marriage. You can advise the other person without becoming emotionally involved, reminding yourself to keep cool and controlled.

These fortunate individuals who have found the secret of self-adjustment and have made a successful job of *overhauling themselves* generally succeed in handling others successfully. Their knowledge of human nature enables them to get along with almost anyone. When confronted with a situation too difficult for them to handle, they have the intelligence to seek competent advice.

• *Get Help if You Need It*

The last step in saving a bad marriage is to consult some psychiatrist in your community if you have tried everything else and failed. He will most likely help you arrive at a decision commensurate with the particular circumstances of your case. Remember that he is better equipped than you are to decide what your next step should be. At least you can feel that you have done everything possible to avoid the wretched consequences of a divorce.

• *Neurotics Seldom Blame Themselves*

George, a young engineer, came for advice regarding the best way of handling his wife, whom he described as being "selfish, spoiled, and a hypochondriac." He stated that Ruth had been an only child, had always been given her way, and was inclined to be overaggresive. She even boasted about being able to get anything she wanted. While still in her teens, Ruth made up her mind to get a certain man. She succeeded in getting him to marry her. However, when she tried to dominate him, he found her intolerable and left for Reno. Following her divorce Ruth married George and once more she gave vent to hysterical episodes of rage, subjecting her husband to unnecessary abuse. She was extremely sensitive. When George came home from work, she nagged him about little things, and displayed unreasonable jealousy whenever he acted friendly at a social gathering.

In the meantime, she was always ailing, changed doctors frequently, and complained about everything from migraine headaces to pains in her feet. As time went on, George began to assert himself. He expressed his intolerance by refusing to cater to her neurotic whims.

In talking with her, she attempted to convince me that

George was a weakling trying to make a mother out of her — that he did not wish to assume the responsibilities of married life and was anything but a man in the technique of love-making. Part of this was true. He had been passive, shy, and inclined to shirk his duties as a husband. However, she didn't help matters by belittling him. She was made to learn that the projection of hostility on to her husband was merely a cover for the guilt she unconsciously experienced because of her own shortcomings as a wife. The neurotic wife or husband always lays the blame for the unhappy marriage on the other person. They seldom blame themselves.

Nevertheless George and Ruth came to a realization that their only way of salvaging their marriage was to rid themselves of the respective neurotic traits that were hangovers from their neurotic childhoods.

They made concessions to each other and discussed their disagreement without becoming emotionally upset. It made all the difference in the world. George had fewer doctor bills to pay and Ruth found an inner tranquility that she had never experienced before. She became less egocentric and enjoyed traveling as a passenger rather than behind the wheel of marriage, once her husband had learned to be an expert driver.

• The Average Marriage

The majority of marriages fortunately fall into the average group. In the average marriage the couples get along fairly well. The husband and wife have learned to adjust themselves to each other. Their disagreements are not too serious; they may not boast of complete happiness, but neither are they particularly unhappy. Their marriage brings them *fifty* to *seventy-five* per cent contentment, which is usually centered around home-ownership, education of their children, insurance against economic and health insecurity, periodic vacations, a circle of friends, and a mutual agreement to accept courageously whatever comes their way.

• How to Stay Happily Married

Many of the unhappy strains that arise in marriage can be

avoided if husband and wife adopt a philosophy of mutual consideration. Every good philosophy needs practical, everyday expression to keep it alive.

Here are some of the working suggestions I have found helpful for couples who want not only to stay married—but to make their marriage a deepening pleasure.

1. Limit criticism to a minimum. Try to understand the psychology of the other sex. There are characteristics of both sexes that have been handed down to us from the beginning of time. For example, most men like to feel important. They like to be flattered, encouraged, and inspired. Many women make the fatal mistake of belittling their husbands, instead of letting them feel they are the most important person in the family. Psychiatrists refer to the process of a wife subjugating her husband to her will as castration." In this respect the wife defeats only herself. She loses the love of her husband and begins to despise herself. Normal women do not wish to dominate a man. Most of them prefer to regard their husbands as their protectors.

   There are also things peculiar to women that men fail to appreciate. Women want to feel secure. You can't abuse a wife and get away with it. Something will always happen. Women are like flowers that need nature and sunshine. They want to be treated as sweethearts and complimented occasionally. Material security is not enough. They want to feel loved and be made to feel that they are responsible in part for their husband's success. Men should realize also that wives do not like to play the mother role to their husbands. They want to look up to a man, to respect him for his masculinity. A husband cannot act like a child and expect his wife to respect him. A man is expected to be a man in every sense of the word, even if he can only act the role.

2. Adopt a courtroom technique for arguments: make them discussions. It takes two people to engage in an argument. If you can't discuss your differences, keeping your emotions under control, don't discuss them at all. Usually they are

of little importance, anyhow. At least wait until you have cooled off or have trained yourself to speak without being abusive and personal. You must learn to distinguish between an argument and a peaceful discussion. If the other person insists on arguing, refuse to imitate what you know to be neurotic.

3. Give conversation its due: make it enjoyable by cutting down on recitals of complaints, ailments, bills, and worries. The average person rebels against one who is always faultfinding, who is continually ailing and running to doctors, who gripes about his or her job and responsibilities at home.

4. Put a stop to sulks, profanity, and name-calling before they become a habit.

5. Examine yourself for your own failings when you are tempted to brood over your partner's.

6. Kill that impulse to rouse suspicion and jealousy in the partner with reports of flirtatious encounters.

7. Have fun, but have it together; marriage falls flat without shared good times to give it sparkle.

8. In case of infidelity, treat it as you would a family illness. Don't shoot. Don't reach for the sleeping pills or the bottle. Don't go running to a lawyer for a quick divorce. Consult a marriage counselor. Because wives are more often the sufferers from a betrayal than husbands, they should have a correspondingly strong interest in learning the reasons for infidelity — and the ways of preventing it.

Prevention is the wisest cure. Here, much depends on the wife. She is the pivotal figure in the home. If she is aware of the stress of the times, the tensions, and the competition her husband must meet, she can offset much of the strain with a kind and tolerant personality.

The qualities are her most effective defense of her family's security. They draw and hold like the warmth of a hearthfire in the cold and dark of night.

9. Make marriage a partnership. It implies co-operation and not a competitive struggle for supremacy. You can't mold the other person into your way of thinking about everything. Despite the fact that there is a husband-wife relationship, each is still a free-thinking in-dividual and entitled to preserve certain rights as a person. Domination is tyranny. The com-bination of a dominating husband and a sub-missive wife is incompatible with intelligence. A normal husband and wife respect the other partner as an intelligent, sensitive human being. You cannot own another person as you own an automobile. Love that is that possessive is ab-normal. True love is altruistic in quality and incorporates the wishes of the beloved partner.

10. If there is any sexual incompatibility present, something should definitely be done about it. Couples who don't get along physically are usually the ones who are constantly bickering. A frigid wife is apt to be sadistic and difficult to live with. A husband who is sexually in-adequate may become a whiner, always com-plaining about his poor health. There is no excuse today for sexual unhappiness. There are books containing scientifically oriented sexual information that can be read, and psychiatrists are available to help you if your sexual problem is a complicated one.

11. To be happy you must find yourself in relation-ship to people and the world about you. You should not depend for your happiness entirely upon the other person. You should cultivate sufficient outside interests to make your married life stimulating. We admire people who are self-sustaining. No one likes a clinging vine of either sex. Learn to sew, read books, listen to music, develop a hobby of some kind, join a club, take a course at some university — *do something.* Unhappy people in marriage are lazy. They al-ways have an excuse for their unhappiness. The majority of them will tell you: "My whole life would have been different if I had married

someone else." One must guard against alibis of this kind. Too many neurotic husbands and wives take the attitude that they are trapped, doomed to unhappiness because the other partner will not change. They must change *themselves* before they can expect a change in *others*.

Session 15.

██

How Necessary Is Sex?

• *Sex and Health*

Sex plays a far more important role in your physical and mental health than you are aware of or willing to admit. One of the dominating factors of life is your sexual instinct made up primarily of two components:

1. A primitive urge to *reproduce*.
2. An aesthetic impulse to *love*.

Freud referred to this sex-drive as "Libido." He contended that many of our mental and nervous disturbances can be traced to sexual repressions — pent-up emotional tensions in need of release.

• *Sex-Happiness is Related to Personality-Happiness*

Emotional health is dependent upon an intelligent management of the sexual aspect of your life.

"Next to hunger, the most powerful of human instincts is that of sex," wrote the late Dr. Peter Marshall. "You cannot escape from it, for you are made that way. It pulses in your blood, sings in your throat, and shines in your eyes. Sex will be either the nicest thing in your life — or it will be the nastiest — depending on whether you use it or abuse it."

People indulge in sexual activities not merely for the

157

happiness of parenthood, but also as an expression of love and for the pleasure and gratification it affords. Many of the achievements in art, music, literature, and science have been inspirationally rooted in the expression or sublimation of the sexual impulse.

Conversely, much unhappiness has been the result of frustrations arising directly or indirectly from sexual difficulties, It has been estimated for example, that four-fifths of all divorces are caused by sexual incompatibility.

• Sex-Sickness Causes Body-Sickness

Sexual disorders are also capable of producing numerous psychosomatic ills.

Exaggerated feelings of guilt in connection with what you do and even *think* sexually can make you ill. The sickness of the soul becomes the sickness of the body. It is not actually what you do sexually, but, rather, the *self-inflicted guilt,* that makes you sick. Sex-guilt may be entirely unconscious. You may say, "I don't feel guilty about anything I've done." But the symptoms that take you to the doctor's office are telling a different story.

• The Need for Sex Enlightenment

In most cases sexual maladjustments had their real start far back in life, in childhood. That is why sex education is so *necessary*, in any plan for good living. Thanks to pioneers like Freud, Stekel, and others, who exposed the interrelationship between sex and health, we are aware of the need for sex enlightenment. Enlightenment means the end of much unnecessary suffering.

Our social prudery regarding sexual matters has its origin in ancient taboos that contravene logic and experience. Sexual ignorance is a grievous folly — a costly delusion that condemns thousands of lives to unnecessary unhappiness.

• Sex-Ignorance Is Costly

The widespread ignorance of one of the most important aspects of human behavior has left in its wake a disastrous toll of human misery. It accounts in part for the unscientific, salacious, and so-called "comic book" treatment of sexual matters in the widely disseminated trashy literature on sex. And it bars constructive measures that a well-informed society could undertake toward clearing-up millions of sexual maladjustments.

• The Need to Be Realistic

Our present social attitude toward sex should be a *realistic* one. The importance of sex enlightenment as a necessary step toward successfully challenging the increasing incidence of sexual maladjustments is aptly expressed by Robert MacIver, Professor of Sociology, Columbia University, who writes:

> We should not be afraid of the truth about human behavior. Knowledge of the facts won't cause immorality, but it will remove false fears and unwise expectations. It will show what are true dangers and what are imaginary ones. We all agree that unenlightened guidance is bad where physical health is concerned. We must learn that it is no less bad when moral health is the issue. Only through knowledge of the facts can we deal intelligently with the serious problems of personality that arise in the area of sexual relations.[1]

When needed education in the principals of sex becomes universal, mankind will pass a milestone of medical progress. A healthier world, inhabited by healthier generations will be the reward, for this is the social purpose of science.

• Sexual Inadequacy in the Male (Impotence)

Dr. Wilhelm Stekel, world famous authority, wrote:

> In men *love-inadequacy* is increasing to an alarming degree, and impotence has come to be a disorder associated with modern civilization. Every impotent man forms the nucleus of a love-tragedy. For impotence makes marriage impossible or may be the cause of an ill-fated one; it also undermines the health of the woman, and has an equally pernicious

---

[1] MacIver, R., *Sex and Social Attitudes, About the Kinsey Report*. New American Library of World Literature, Inc., New York: 1948.

effect upon the mental health of both husband and
wife. The percentage of relatively impotent men
cannot be placed too high. In my experience, hardly
half of all civilized men enjoy normal potency.

Causative Factors in Impotence. The problem of impotence
is a very *complex* one, mainly because there are many variations and degrees of impotence. In the majority of cases, impotence is due to *psychological* factors. It represents the symp-
tom-consequence of some deep-seated unresolved conflict or
may be the result of inhibitory influences—bashfulness, sex-
ignorance, fear, guilt feelings, disgust, unhappiness, sudden
indisposition, inability to love, insecurity, faulty attitudes
toward sex, self-pity, masochism or psychic invalidism, homosexual repressions, bisexual conflicts, sadism (desire to punish
the partner), fear of causing a woman pain, fear of making a
woman pregnant, fear of being interrupted during the sex
act, conflicts involving religious or parental censure, jealousy,
hostility, and numerous other causes.

Premature Ejaculation. Hasty ejaculation is the most common type of sexual inadequacy. It involves unsuccessful
coitus, leaving the woman unsatisfied. It is generally caused
by a conflict between the urge to gratify one's sexual desire
and an opposing force—the inhibition of such an urge.

Sexual Apathy. Sexual indifference is another form of impotence.

Impotence problems may be responsible for a multiplicity
of health-complaints, and invariably influence one's personality.

Impotent men often become *hypochondriacs.* They go to
many doctors, suffering from a variety of ailments — insomnia, fatigue, depression, lack of appetite, indigestion, headaches, nervousness, and tension, and are difficult to get along
with.

Husbands who suffer from impotence feel quite guilty that
they are unable to adequately satisfy their wives. They are
embarrassed and humiliated when their attempts end in
failure. Wives are cautioned not to berate, ridicule, or humili-
ate their husbands because of their sexual inadequacy. Re-

actions of disappointment only makes matters worse and makes the husband feel more inferior, inadequate, and guilty, which in turn enhances his symptoms.

Impotence caused by factors deeply rooted in the unconscious require psychiatric treatment. The prognosis is essentially good. The duration of treatment depends on each individual case. Some cases of impotence respond favorably to a short-term analysis, while others require deep psychological therapy over a prolonged period of time.

• Sexual Inadequacy in the Female (Frigidity)

Frigidity is a *symptom-disturbance* in the psychosexual development of women, causing them to find it difficult to achieve a *vaginal orgasm* during sexual intercourse. It is the most common sexual disorder among women. One investigator reports that 40 per cent of all married women derive little or no pleasure from the sexual act.

Incidentally, frigidity does not necessarily refer to *sexual coldness* to sex relations on the part of a woman, as the term might imply.

Frigid women are blocked from enjoying sex because of their inhibitions, repressions, and inability to give vent to the full expression of their sexual cravings. Frigidity in one sense is a form of self-denial.

There are many *types* of frigidity. The causes depend upon the type involved.

Relative Frigidity.—This refers to an *orgasm-incapacity* caused by a sexually inadequate husband. When the husband's problem is corrected and his technique is improved, the wife is able to experience satisfaction.

Pseudo-Frigidity.—This is a type caused by inhibition, prudishness, false modesty, fears of various kinds, and sex ignorance. With proper reeducation of attitudes and adequate insight into the complexes interfering with their response, these women can soon develop the capacity for enjoyable sex relations.

Narcissistic Frigidity.—This is a more extreme kind of

frigidity. An example is the beautiful woman who regards sex as something *sordid*. She wishes there was no necessity for having to give herself to her husband. Menstruation is usually regarded by such a person as the "curse." Some beautiful women are frigid. They are in love with themselves—in love with their face and body—and are unable to concentrate during the sexual act. Their mind is on other things.

Beautiful Women in Love with Themselves. I have interviewed several female patients whose income as professional models was quite high. Their husbands complained about their indifference to sex. Many beautiful women who have been greatly flattered believe that all men are alike—they all have a "line." Being conditioned to constant flattery, they develop a fixation of their "libido" at the *narcissistic* level. They are unable to forget that they are beautiful. During sex relations they are more concerned about trying to keep their hair from being disheveled than getting satisfaction out of the sex act itself.

One wife applied fingernail polish on her nails during marital relations. Her husband had known that his wife was sexually cold, but never thought that she was that indifferent to the act. Another husband told me that his wife continued to read a book while having sex relations. Still another desired to have her baby delivered by a Caesarian operation rather than the natural way, because she did not want her sex anatomy changed in any way.

A strikingly beautiful girl, married for the third time, was referred to me for a psychiatric appraisal of her health-complaints. She complained of severe headaches, fatigue, and physical discomforts. When I questioned her about her sex life she appeared quite embarrassed and was reluctant to discuss the matter with me. Finally she told me she was still a virgin. I asked her what she meant. She said that she never allowed any of the three husbands to have sex relations with her. She considered sex "sordid."

Guilt Can Cause a Woman to be Frigid. Many women who because of harboring some past or present guilt in connection with sex, are unable to abandon themselves to the pleasures of the sex act.

Women who are promiscuous are apt to suffer from orgasm-incapacity because of guilt resulting from their dissipations.

Hostility Interferes with Sexual Responsiveness. A wife who harbors strong feelings of hostility toward her husband would naturally find it more difficult to achieve orgasms than one who *loves* her husband.

Frigidity usually develops in women who are belligerent, nervous, tense, and unrelaxed. Many of them are unable to concentrate during sexual relationship with their husbands.

Frigid wives as a result of their lack of sexual satisfaction are generally *sadistic.* They nag and quarrel over trivialities. Almost all frigid women are highly nervous, neurotic personalities.

The "Will to Displeasure." Women who are unable to find satisfaction in sex relations do not know the subconscious reason for it. Some believe they are *born* frigid and are resigned to their fate. They carry out their physical obligations in a mechanical, apathetic sort of way—as a *duty* rather than as something really desired. Dr. Wilhelm Stekel calls this the "will to displeasure." The so-called virgin-wife is actually saying in the language of her subconscious—"I must give myself as a dutiful wife, but you can't make me find satisfaction in it."

• Husbands Are Sometimes to Blame

Many husbands are so inadequate at being good sexual partners that they are responsible for their wives turning against sex. A wife must depend on her husband for instruction in all sex matters. But many husbands are poor teachers. They are too restrained themselves. Dr. Louis Bisch claims a woman is like a fine musical instrument. He advises: "Learn to *play* it and you get the *music* you desire." Most men believe that sex is purely physical. According to Dr. Bisch the mental and emotional correlates are decidedly more important.

It is often impossible for the wife to be a satisfactory sexual partner if the husband is inadequate. Consequently it is a husband's duty to seek professional guidance if he is inexperienced and to insist that his wife investigate the cause of her frigidity, particularly because sex satisfaction is so essential to a successful marriage.

• *Homosexuality*

Homosexuality today constitutes one of the most important sociological problems of modern civilization. It exists among persons in all walks of life—the poor and the rich, the ignorant and the intellectual, the unmarried and the married, the young and the old.

Homosexuality is a *symptom* of a deep-rooted neurosis that can be traced to the development of a neurotic relationship to certain members of the family. It is neither an inherited condition nor a disease-entity. Medical evidence tends to disprove the existence of any glandular cause for homosexuality. It is an acquired form of sex behavior, resulting from *psychological* rather than physical forces. While homosexuals are virile and physically healthy, possessing normal sex organs, they are unable to experience a normal desire for the opposite sex. There are those of course, who are bisexual and capable of experiencing sex relations with either sex. Many of them marry in order to camouflage their homosexual inclinations. Some marry with the hope that marriage will serve as a solution to their homosexual problem — that as long as they have access to heterosexual relations they are less likely to find homosexual activities inviting.

Causes of Homosexuality. There is no single theory that can adequately explain the cause of this aberration. What may cause one person to become a homosexual may not hold true for another. Whether or not a child develops homosexual tendencies is dependent upon a number of contributory factors — the influence of his parents, experiences of a sexual nature during childhood and early adolescence, feelings of inferiority associated with specific handicaps, and personal relations to the home environment; also a susceptibility to influences within the community and exposures to situations which threaten one's sense of security, such as the death of a mother or father, parental incompatibility resulting in the divorce of the parents, and influences of parents who are neurotic or psychopathic.

To psychoanalysis we are indebted for a better understanding of the psychology of homosexuality. It has been demonstrated, for example, that homosexual patterns in men often develop as a result of a son's strong attachment to his mother — what Freud called the "Oedipus complex." A male child may develop feminine traits because he identifies himself with his mother or sister and imitates them. Parents sometimes encourage these identifications among their children, not realizing the possible consequences to their sexual development. Regarding such patterns in children, Clara Thompson informs us:

> A very important determining influence in the development of homosexuality is the child's awareness that his sex was a disappointment to the parent's or to the most important parent, especially if their disappointment leads them to treat the child as if he were of the opposite sex.[1]

Mothers are sometimes guilty of infecting their sons with too much "momism," to use Dr. Strecker's term. These over-solicitous "Moms" fail to appreciate that excess love showered on a male child is equivalent to too many lumps of sugar in a cup of coffee. It becomes sickeningly sweet. Boys rebel against mothers who try to make husband-substitutes out of them. They refuse to be looked on as sissies by other boys. It is this basic feeling of inferiority in the male child, fostered by a mother who means well but nevertheless does harm, that accounts for the development of a homosexual pattern in adolescence and adult life.

Homosexuality is a Manifestation of Sexual Immaturity. Homosexuals are for the most part sexually immature, neurotic, children at heart, love-starved, and frustrated. They are inclined to fear the opposite sex. Their sex behavior represents

---

[1] Clara Thompson, *Changing Concepts of Homosexuality, A Study of Interpersonal Relations,* edited by Patrick Mullahy (New York: Hermitage Press, 1949).

a regression to childhood, an escape from the biological responsibilities assumed by one who is heterosexual. They are *narcissistic,* insofar as their own pleasures come first, irrespective of what others think about their conduct.

Homosexuals Do not Understand Their Unconscious Motivations. Homosexuals as a group do not understand their "unconscious." Hence they find it difficult to discipline themselves successfully. Many of the overt homosexuals deny experiencing a sense of guilt, but they suffer from a multiplicity of neurotic ailments for which they seek medical aid. They may complain of states of depression, headaches, fatigue, insomnia, digestive disturbances, pains around the heart, fainting spells, dizziness, and so forth. They go to their physician for relief, not appreciating the role that anxiety and guilt associated with their homosexuality play in the development of their symptom-complaints. Occasionally homosexual experiences may result in the precipitation of a *psychosis.* This in itself is reason enough why homosexuals need psychiatric treatment.

Pseudo-Narcissism. In an attempt to overcompensate for feelings of inferiority many homosexuals develop a pseudo-narcissism (false feelings of superiority). They constitute the pseudo-intellectuals who prefer to live in Bohemian sections of a large city and dabble in art and literature. Although some are quite talented and gifted, there are many who never achieve any degree of success because of their underlying chronic frustration and unhappiness. They rationalize their homosexuality by claiming that some of the world's greatest artists and writers have been homosexuals.

Proper sex education made accessible in our schools and universities can do much to prevent homosexuality.

Conditions that are psychological in origin can only be treated successfully by psychological methods. Hence psychoanalysis today offers the homosexual the greatest hope for a lasting cure. The homosexual must be made to understand the psychological causes of his affliction.

● *Miscellaneous Sex Deviations*

There are many sexual aberrations that specifically require psychiatric treatment. These involve sex offenses committed by persons suffering from serious sexual maladjustments and include cases of rape, "Peeping Tomism," the molesting of children, indecent exposure (exhibitionism), and other types of offenses.

What Is Normal and Abnormal in Sex? Married couples discuss financial problems regularly. They will also discuss problems involving their children, or where to spend their vacation. But the all-important basis of their marriage — their sexual relation — is rarely discussed.

Both wives and husbands come to me complaining of the partner's sex technique. They want to know if this activity or that is abnormal. Or they may be worried because they want a kind of love-play that the partner might consider abnormal. Too embarrassed or fearful to speak of it, the wife or husband tries to repress the desire and the marital relation becomes unsatisfying.

They ask, "Where is the line between normal and abnormal to be drawn? Who is to have the final say as to what is acceptable sex play and what is not?"

There Is no Absolute "Norm" in Sex Activity. There is no hard and fast rule. What is normal for one man may be shocking to another. In marital relations, these things are matters of taste and inclination.

The sexual appetite, like the appetite for food, is satisfied by different things in different people. Which man or woman can be said to be normal; the one who prefers an undeviatingly plain meal, or the one who wants spice and variety in food?

Both are normal. If a husband and wife are happily married, whatever they do to express physical love and give happiness to each other within reason is normal. Deviations are allowable as long as they lead to normal intercourse. They are abnormal and neurotic, in most cases, if they are always practiced to the *exclusion* of the natural mating intended by nature.

It is the purpose that determines much of the allowability in sex play. Much love and sex play is childish, like the absurdities of love talk, but the purpose of the playfulness puts the activity into the right context. If variation in love-making produces a better result, it is better to accommodate your partner, provided the activity is acceptable to you.

The normal person never develops a craving for extreme combinations in sex, any more than he does in his food. He may prefer spicy to plain food, but he is not likely to try anything as bizarre as maple syrup on oysters. He is too adult. The sexually neurotic, starved for some lasting sensation of satisfaction, is likely to try anything.

Maritally, it is just as normal not to be interested in varia-tions in the relationship as it is to prefer plain food to the exotic. On the whole, however, the more intelligent prefer to make something fine of their love relationship, varying it enough to keep it out of the humdrum.

• *You Can Plan for Happier Sex*

The man and wife who want to keep their sex relationship a joy will groom for it, plan for it. They prefer esthetic sur-roundings. Avoiding monotony, they tease and play and linger and enjoy it, which is not only the intelligent way, but also the natural way.

Thinking about sex activities is a normal and inevitable part of married life. Many husbands and wives, in thinking of their relationship, may think of change. They may come to long for such a change, yet fear that the partner would regard it as abnormal.

The psychiatrist feels that the expression of these desires for variety is healthier than keeping them repressed. Many divorces could be prevented if the husband and wife adopted this attitude, and discussed their mutual desires frankly with each other.

• The Right and Wrong Approach

Every case of sexual variations must be judged on its own individual merits. The so-called normal varieties of sex play between husband and wife have a right and a wrong way to be approached. If a husband wants to perform a certain act in love and is crude or unpleasant in his approach or rides roughshod over his partner's feelings in the matter, then his wife is opposed to the deviation. Eventually, she becomes opposed to all marital relations with him.

If a man is cruel or mean, whatever he does becomes repulsive to her. Yet a considerate lover can make the same act a pleasure.

• Couples Must Decide for Themselves

No generalities can be made as to exactly what is morally or ethically right for any particular case. These things have to be decided by the individual. The psychiatrist can only educate to the intelligent attitude, the right approach to sex. The questioner must make up his own mind.

A neurotic attitude toward deviations in normal sex play can produce actual impotence in the husband. He may become so inhibited either by his own worry about his desires or by his wife's rejections that he can't act the role of the husband. In the same way, a wife can become numb to the husband's lovemaking because she can't be frank enough with him to tell him what makes her happy and what does not.

• Neurotic Inhibitions

Even in this modern era, many people are brought up with great severity as far as the attitude toward sex is concerned. Too many warnings from fearful parents can make grown sons and daughters afraid to use their own judgment in the field of sex, even after marriage. Even variations in kissing are considered shocking and abnormal by those so brought up. As a result these people become inhibited and stiff and make poor marital partners.

• It's All in Your Attitude

A great deal of what is considered deviation in sex practice is highly *relative*. We have in our culture, in our time, decided on the heterosexual union as the *ideal* and only *acceptable* form of sex activity. Yet even within the framework of the heterosexual union, there are practices that investigations, such as those of Kinsey, show to be looked upon differently by different people.

• Sex and Love in Marriage

When we speak of sex, we do not mean simply the physical act alone. When we say sex, we also imply *emotional security,* because sex and love are intermingled. Sex is only the outward symbol of the need to give and receive love. *Sex-frustration* means *love-frustration*. Together they spell insecurity. A human being who goes through life denied love can never feel secure. Love is the bony structure of our whole emotional life. Without it, life collapses.

Sex in marriage is a *togetherness*—a time of private lovemaking when hopeful plans are made and shared together, a time when little misunderstandings are swept away in a mutual love.

Mutual physical and mental adaptation between partners with an equality of desire produces sexual harmony—the foundation of a happy marriage.

Many couples during five, ten, or more years of married life never become sexually adjusted, simply because neither of them has taken the initiative to do something about their sexual maladjustment. The first year of every marriage should be a probationary period, physically and psychologically. After that something should be done about incompatible relations, whether sexual or emotional.

Too many married couples begin to take the sex relationship for granted after the first year or so of married life.

They become slipshod about it. They don't give it its proper importance as something *inspiring* and *pleasurable*. They are too apt to dismiss it as a matter of habit, of biological necessity.

• *Make the Most of Sex Happiness*

Every married couple should capitalize on the sex relationship to relax and refresh their marriage, to renew the bonds.

How a husband and wife harmonize in the early years of their marriage will determine the tone of their relationship for perhaps 20 or 30 years as they grow older together.

This much of a life-span is too important to let deteriorate. Our emotional relationships in later years are like retirement pay—they are the return on our life's work. An ideal relationship in marriage is not only a joy while you have it, it is like an investment fund that is returned with interest when you most need it.

• *Think Right about Sex*

Attitude is all-important in understanding and correcting sex troubles. The right attitude plus knowledge of the subject add up to the best sex adjustment you can achieve. Your first step toward that goal is realizing the importance of sex in your life—not as a physical act alone, but an integral part of everything you do.

The way you behave sexually is an expression of your inner personality. It is not a thing apart. It is a powerful force, because it is blended inextricably with emotion, with what we call the *love-impulse*. It has the greatest power for good in our lives when we understand it. It has the greatest power for inflicting suffering, if we abuse the physical or neglect the emotional aspect.

• *Educate Yourself in Sex Matters*

There are two ways to acquire a better understanding of sex. One is through cooperative learning with your partner— through frank discussion and *shared study of good books on the subject.* There are books ranging from the very simple, elementary treatment, to the more advanced technical and scientific studies.

Some argue that if two persons love each other, they need not read books on sex. They say that the Indians never had sex instruction—that our grandmothers never read any books on sex. This is an irrational argument, because it would be difficult to estimate the extent of sexual frustrations that existed among people living many years ago. The women apparently lacked common sense that should have prompted them to complain about it. They were satisfied doing the cooking and raising the children. They did not consider a sexual climax important. They were more servile and restrained in those days. Today, women are more intelligent about these matters. They are able to recognize serious sexual disorders such as impotence and frigidity and can appreciate the inner relationship between nervous disorders and sexual deprivation or frustration. Modern women understand the importance of being sexually gratified as well as being properly supported economically. At the same time, it appears that there are more complaints about frigidity than ever before. That is because women are admitting that something is wrong sexually and want help and advice. Many women will not tolerate sexual incompatibility, which in turn influences the divorce rate.

● *Seek Advice*

The other way of gaining better understanding of sex is through outside consultation. People who have had little formal education or who find reading no help to them can take their sexual problem to their clergyman or family doctor. In most cases, a man of either calling can give advice in simple language. He may recommend visits to a marriage counselor, a clinic, or a psychiatrist.

● *Summing It All Up*

The important thing to remember is the need to know all

you can about this aspect of your life. It is actually an aspect of *self-survival*. To survive, you need not only food and shelter, but also spiritual sustenance. You need to live emotionally, as well as physically. Because our sex life is basically important to our health, and because our health is the foundation of our daily life, we need to keep alert to new discoveries in the field of sex knowledge.

This does not mean that we should emphasize sex for sex' sake, or pleasure for pleasure's sake. Even a good sex life cannot work miracles, but it is a good foundation and inspiration for achieving what you want to in life. *Better sex means an increased capacity for love and tolerance and a better relationship with family, friends, and business associates. It lends poise and a relaxed outlook that is communicated to all around you.*

Session 16.

Getting Rid of Fears
That Make You Sick

• Types of Fears

Fear is a universal human reaction that is biologically justified by the protection it provides for the individual in the
event of danger. It is an emotion experienced when an individual is confronted with a definite threat to life and limb.
Fear, wrote Leon Mones, is the stop-look-and-listen, warning
of life.

In the world today, the human spirit is confronted on every
side with warnings and threats that justly call for caution.
With the experiencing of fear, there is set in motion a large
number of psychosomatic reactions, the sole purpose of which
is to help the person escape or combat danger. In situations
that threaten us or menace our chances for happiness or success, the feeling at the pit of the stomach, that dampness of
the palms, that pounding of the heart, that leadenness of
movement and stammering of speech—in short, the feeling of
fear, may well beset all of us.

• People React Differently to Fear-Producing
Situations

Not all persons respond in the same way to fear-producing

situations. Some people ordinarily unafraid of dogs are frightened by their barking, while other individuals remain undisturbed. Then there are those who do not mind thunder and lightning, taking these phenomena as a matter of course; others are very much frightened by lightning and thunder.

Although fear is experienced in the presence of a definite danger (*normal type of fear*), and although we might say the degree of fear experienced is exactly proportional to the degree of danger present, instances are nevertheless observed when the objective cause of fear appears negligible, yet the fear reaction may be so marked as to virtually precipitate a panic (*neurotic type of fear*). Such a fear, one that is wholly out of proportion to the stimulus, is of the nature of a neurotic reaction, and we speak of these as "phobias." One individual may be "frightened to death" on seeing a black cat; another may be precipitated into a frenzy on seeing birds.

• Common Phobias

The following is a sample list of some common phobias:

Claustrophobia—dread of narrow and closed places
Hydrophobia—dread of water
Ailurophobia—dread of cats
Anthrophobia—dread of men
Pathophobia—dread of disease
Microphobia—dread of germs
Phthisiophobia—dread of tuberculosis
Zoophobia—dread of animals
Misophobia—dread of dirt
Syphilophobia—dread of syphilis
Sitophobia—dread of food
Acrophobia—dread of heights
Agoraphobia—dread of open spaces
Phobophobia—fear of being afraid

• A Simple Phobia

A *simple phobia* is a *conditioned reaction due to some early unpleasant experience, such as having been frightened by a dog, a snake, or a mouse.* The patient relives the fear-producing episode of his past. For instance, a patient told me how at the age of 12, she discovered a small dead mouse under her pillow. She was frightened and screamed. Her brother had placed it there as a prank. Ever since this particular episode she feels compelled to look under her pillow each night before retiring. She claims she has a greater phobia for a mouse than for an unfriendly dog.

• *A Complex Phobia*

A *complex phobia* is *one associated with a conflict that has been repressed or buried in the unconscious.* The patient protects himself or herself from the *real* fear by taking on a *substitute* fear. For example, an unmarried girl who has a morbid fear of dirt (misophobia) and finds it necessary to wash her hands more than the usual number of times, may actually be suffering from a fear of *moral contamination.* The latter constitutes the unconscious or *true* fear.

• *What Is a Superstition?*

There is a relation between fear and superstition. A superstition may be spoken of as a *crystallized fear.* Thus some individuals regard it as a fearful omen if they are crossed by a black cat, while others think that Friday the 13th is a day laden with a dark future. "Keeping your fingers crossed" or "knocking on wood" will never influence the outcome of anything. Many educated people are superstitious. According to Karl R. Stolz, one-half of all college graduates of this country entertain superstitions.

• *Unreal Fears*

An unreal or neurotic fear is an apprehensive fear about something that does not exist at the time. Something is wrong with the warning system, the red light keeps blinking, you are bewildered, and things harmless in themselves take on a dangerous aspect. A talk with the boss becomes an occasion of dread and foreboding. A request to make an unplanned speech finds you unable to utter a sound. A slightly off-taste meal, even in a reputable restaurant, makes you think you are poisoned, and you promptly become sick with anxiety.

I know a young man who had panics regularly, each time without an ascribable reason and each time taking the form of terror of dying. He has now conquered his panic attacks, having learned their nature and cause.

• What Do Phobias Symbolize?

Phobias are escape mechanisms from inner conflicts. There are about eighty to one hundred known phobias. They constitute fears that are illogical and absurd and are generally associated with forgotten or repressed experiences that are usually unpleasant.

They are considered "substituted emotions," and sometimes are spoken of as "repressed neuroses." The abnormal fear represents a *symbol* of something that is unpleasant, and that has been repressed. In other words, the phobia serves a definite function. It is intended to disguise or displace an entirely different fear, one that is too painful to our consciousness. It represents a running away from some inner psychic conflict. A fear of thunder may symbolize a fear of recalling how a father would shout at the mother in profane terms, or how the father would manifest terrific outbursts of anger. These fears or "emotional distortions" can be traced to early repressed experiences. They cause chronic states of anxiety and prove quite distressing. The anxiety overruns into physical channels, which in turn aggravates the phobia, and a vicious cycle is established.

• A Case of Cardiophobia

Nancy, age 27, suffered from *cardiophobia* (fear of heart disease). She insisted that she had heart disease and would die of a fatal heart attack. Physical examination and electrocardiograms were negative. She expressed a fear that God would bring about her death.

I learned that for six months she had nursed a secret love

for her neighbor's husband. The neighbor, a woman in her late thirties, was ill with cancer. Nancy had hoped she would die. Cancer finally did cause the woman's death, and shortly afterwards Nancy succeeded in marrying the widower. Several months following the marriage, she began to experience acute states of anxiety and expressed a fear that she would die suddenly. She became obsessed with the feeling that she was the cause of her neighbor's death.

The phobia involving her heart served as an outlet for her guilt (a self-punitive mechanism). Nancy was made to understand the psychology of her phobia and responded well to psychotherapy, with the result that her anxiety symptoms disappeared.

• A Case-Illustration of Acrophobia

A married man consulted me because of his *acrophobia* (fear of heights). He also complained of dizziness, headaches, and nausea. He had been given a complete physical examination and nothing organic could be found to account for his symptoms.

His unmarried daughter had become pregnant, and he found it necessary to escort her to a private institution where she gave birth to the child. The child was adopted by an unknown couple and the entire affair was kept a secret. The father and daughter returned home. However, six months later the father learned quite accidentally that several members of his community knew about his daughter having been pregnant out of wedlock.

It was shortly afterwards that he began to entertain a pronounced fear of heights. He was afraid to look out of a window because his office was located on the sixth floor. Although he denied suicidal thoughts or inclinations, it was later revealed that his acrophobia represented actually a fear of suicide disguised by a fear of heights to escape disgrace.

• Phobias Cause Anxiety

Finding the cause of the phobia is to understand the symbolization of the morbid or irrational fear. One might ask if a phobia is a protective mechanism for a fear that is more painful, why attempt to eliminate the phobia? Simply because phobias place the patient in a chronic state of anxiety. It is preferable to have the patient abreact (relive) emotionally the original fear, so that he might understand the unconscious motivation of his phobia and thus be relieved of his anxiety symptoms and not left at the neurotic pill-addiction level.

• *Each Phobia Has Its Own Cause*

There exists no stereotyped symbolization chart of phobias. However, we have profited from past experience with patients suffering from similar fears, and, like dreams, we can keep in mind certain diagnostic impressions that are either corroborated or rejected according to supporting evidence. For instance, syphilophobia may be a disguised fear of homosexuality. Misophobia, or a fear of dirt, may represent a fear of moral contamination. Zoophobia may stand for a fear of the father, rather than a fear of animals. Each phobia has its own cause, and therefore each case must be studied separately.

• *Both Real and Neurotic Fears Are Controllable*

The *real* fears can be effectively utilized to insure success in the alarming situation. The fear of future insecurity for ourselves and our dependents leads us to wise buying of sound investments, to building up a bank account, and to maintaining insurance policies. The unreal and groundless fears can be done away with to secure a fuller measure of enjoyment out of life. *Morbid fears are thieves of happiness.*

To conquer morbid fears it is necessary to:

1. Admit your fear;
2. Understand your fear;
3. Do something about it;
4. Keep busy and work at enjoying life;
5. Seek competent guidance, if necessary.

• *Admit Your Fear*

More is involved in acceptance of fear than the mere cataloging of the hazards, real and mock, that you encounter. You must accept the reality of your fear, which is, in a large sense, the reality of life itself. You can't run away from the hobgoblins of the mind—not in drink, not under the pillows, not in convenient illness, and only very expensively in suicide.

When you brave the whole schedule of your fears, you will find most of them disappear. Are you an expectant mother who is developing feelings of uneasiness? Does everything startle you, and have you acquired timidities you never knew before? What do you find in the list of your fears? "I'm afraid to go through that ordeal." Perhaps you have forgotten that you were born quite safely, and so were your friends, their children, and all the children you never even heard of. Ask those mothers, for that's the reality. The reality is that you'll come through in grand style.

• *Understand Your Fear*

The first question you must address to yourself is, "Have I really anything to be afraid of?" If you are chased by a growling dog, your warning system will act to remove you to safety, and you experience a passing scare. You'll probably forget about the whole thing soon. But if your warning system goes off when a mouse darts across your path, you really haven't anything to be afraid of, and you should recognize the fact. If you are about to undergo a dangerous operation, some trepidation is to be expected; if the prospect of a sex experience in a normal and accepted situation causes the same nervousness, you are cheating yourself with an unwarranted fear. If you seem to be afraid of many things, of "everything," set down explicitly on paper the situations and objects that give rise to your disquietudes, and look your bugaboos and scarecrows in the face.

• *Do Something About Your Fears*

Merely knowing what you fear and even admitting that you

are afraid isn't enough. But it is the necessary beginning. What you do about it will be crucial.

If you find by comparing your fears with those that seem to have been warranted that at some particular time you have a valid reason for trepidation, then say, "All right, I'm scared. Where do I go from here?" and go somewhere. In wartime, soldiers have real cause to be afraid, and many of them are extremely frightened for a while. But those who make the grade learn to add up their chances, and they do the job with such concentration and fixity of purpose that they haven't the time to remember to be afraid. In civilian life the magnitude of the dangers we face are usually not very great; the possibilities of avoiding extreme consequences are considerable. However, there are exceptions.

One of my patients, a young girl, learned she was suffering from a fatal disease and that her life would soon be over. After an initial panic she managed to look her problem squarely in the face and came to the conclusion that she would put the relative shortness of her life-expectancy out of her mind. Because a great deal of physical activity was out of the question, and because she needed something to occupy her mind, she chose to study languages, and within six months was competent to assume the job of foreign correspondent for an export house. The remaining years of her life were filled with interesting work and a time consuming avocation. Few, if any, could guess what prospects this girl faced. She herself, almost forgot.

Neurotic fear is an emotional spree. The "victim" may be using the fear to make up for some other lack. A young man I know had an overpowering fear of marriage, especially in its sexual aspects. He used this fear as the vehicle for fantastic imaginings concerning what would happen to him if he indulged in sexual acts, and, of course, the content of these imaginings was a poor substitute for the normal married sex life that he wanted so much. His trouble was that he was afraid any real experience would prove him impotent.

The first thing to do about such fears is: *stop cultivating them.* Treat them as bad habits that must be eliminated, and conscientiously tear them out of your system.

Are you panic stricken if someone requests you to play the piano at a party (when you really play rather well)? Go to parties and play. Play at an audience of friends. If you stumble, don't give up and claim stage-fright or "butter-fingers". After the first few times you won't stumble. A new York psychologist has started a clinic to which people suffering from stage-fright come. Each client performs in front of a jeering, noisy audience that tries to rattle him. After a few such episodes no audience in the world is too much.

Are you afraid of the dark? Turn out the lights in your home and carefully explore it in total darkness. Find out where things are by touch, examine objects you don't readily recognize and make an inventory in your mind. Open the closets and feel for the ghosts. You'll be surprised how scarce ghosts are.

• Keep Busy

Another way to overcome neurotic and groundless fear is to *keep yourself busy.* Idle minds, like idle hands, accomplish no good. This is an extraordinarily complicated world, with facets enough to interest everyone 24 hours a day. The key to really effective utilization of time is *participation,* give and take.

Whether your fears are real or imaginary they will be less awesome if you strive to participate in the great happenings in the world around you. A man who seeks solitude and who wants to escape from the throng, seeks only to nurse his own fears and unhappinesses. If you develop strong ties with the world outside yourself, if you give all the love that is possible for you and accept the love of your world, your own happiness will be assured, and the threat of personal, groundless fears will thereby be banished.

• Seek Help

If by your own efforts you are unable to cope with your

terrors—and there are many of us who are—seek competent guidance. Today, mental illness is seen in the same perspective as physical illness—as a disorder that springs from natural causes and yields to proper treatment. Morbid fears constitute mental illness. Like a broken ankle, they make a cripple of you—a mental cripple. Mentally and emotionally, you limp along in pain and scarcely see the good things in life. Your friendships are affected, your enjoyment is thwarted, and you simply don't get the most out of life.

Nine out of ten people can deal with their own fears, following the rules suggested above. But the tenth, or it may be the hundredth, fails. That is, he fails by himself. If you are that one, you need help. You owe it to yourself, your family, and your friends to take this last step and win for yourself that measure of peace of mind and happiness that is everyone's due.

Session 17.

▄▞▞▞▀

Stop Hating Yourself

• *What Does "Hating" Mean?*

The simplest way to define hate is to say that it is the opposite of love.

Many people who deny hating themselves or others have experienced emotional reactions that were actually *disguised* manifestations of feelings of hatred. There are many who do not like to be accused of hating, because it causes them to feel guilty, and, therefore, psychoanalysts prefer to use the term "hostility," which is more generally acceptable. It carries a less derogatory connotation.

One can think of hate or hostility as a trunk of a tree. Strong dislikes, sarcasm, bitterness, resentments, prejudices, bigotry, stubbornness, sadistic humor and teasing, unfounded accusations, gossip, intolerance, excessive nagging, quarreling, bickering, and acts of violence represent only a few of the many branches of the tree. In its broadest meaning, hating includes anything that tends to hurt ourselves or others.

• *Hate-Reactions Are Sometimes Unconsciously Repressed*

Hate reactions are not always *overtly* expressed. They are often *unconsciously* repressed. Dr. Karl Menninger will long be remembered for his contribution to the better understanding of human nature through his books *The Human Mind,*

184

Man Against Himself, and *Love Against Hate.* He describes the paradox of man striving to improve the world, wanting to live and love, and at the same time giving vent to his unconscious self-destructive impulses via crime, suicide, alcholism, and wars.

It would not be too far-fetched to assume that the ills of civilization can be attributed to man's inability to control his impulse to *hate* and *kill.* The infliction of pain and suffering on ourselves and others, consciously or unconsciously motivated, makes *hatred* in its many disguised forms a *disease*—one more devastating in its influence than *cancer.* Some day wisdom will inspire us to expend the same amount of money, time, and effort toward the scientific study and remedy of *hate* as we are doing at the present time with polio, cancer, and other challenging physical diseases.

• *Why Do People Hate?*

Before you can stop hating you should know something about the *origin* of hate. Many of us develop early patterns of hate during childhood.

Children, for example, develop reactions of hate to parents who either mistreat them or deprive them of a sufficient quantity of the love and affection they seek. No normal child likes to be the recipient of physical pain. Parents who beat their children, encouraged by the rationalization that corporal punishment is the only one that proves effective, are fostering in their children the seeds of hostility.

George Devereux in describing the customs of the Mohave Indians, writes:

> The Mohaves never strike their children or punish them in any way. One who did so would be regarded as "crazy." When asked why he did not respond to the blows administered to him by a child, one of the Mohaves said, "Why should I strike him? I am big, he is small. He cannot hurt me. If I did so I should be like the white people who beat their children."[1]

[1] George Devereux, *Mohave Etiquette* (Los Angeles: Southwest Museum, 1948).

Children need to be restrained and disciplined, but never with measures of violence. Neurotic mothers and fathers are often unaware of the unconscious factors responsible for the sadistic handling of their children. As Dr. Karl Menninger points out,

> Parents often treat their child as they themselves were treated by their own parents, many years previously, thus achieving a long-deferred and displaced revenge for the indignities and suffering they endured. But queerly enough, such parents rarely recognize the hate implied in their behavior. They defend their position with the most respectable rationalizations.[2]

It is these very children who, when they grow up to be adults, project their childhood frustrations in the form of feelings of hostility toward everyone they come in contact with, including their own children. Thus, patterns of hate are frequently passed on from generation to generation.

• Wife-Beaters

I have encountered numerous cases of wives who were the victims of husbands who beat them. Study of these husbands invariably revealed that they had been exposed to a highly neurotic mother or a tyrannical father. Wives who are mistreated by their husbands are naturally prone to develop feelings of hatred, and deliberately or unconsciously provoke greater hostility in the husband. Is it any wonder that children of such parents learn to hate only because they have never been taught to love.

• Freud's Explanation of Hatred

Freud claimed there exists in every human being two opposing instincts—the instinct to love and the self-destructive instinct. This would imply that an infant was *born* to hate. Psychoanalysts refer to this concept of inborn-hatred as the "death instinct theory." There are many psychiatrists today

---

[2] Dr. Karl Menninger, *The Human Mind* (New York: Alfred Knopf, 1937, page 27).

who do not subscribe to this Freudian hypothesis. As I have previously stated, I cannot appreciate the scientific logic behind such a theory. Hate, to my way of thinking, is an *acquired* emotional reaction to ego-insults and anything that threatens our security. No one is *born* to hate. We *learn* to hate. *Fear* on the other hand is something that we *are* born with. It has a self-protective function. *People hate because they are afraid.* Fear makes them feel *insecure* and the greater the insecurity, the greater the tendency to react to threats of any kind with hate. Man was born with only *one* instinct—the instinct of *self-preservation* (to survive, to love).

Nature endowed us with many and varied aspects of this instinct of self-preservation in order to make it possible for us to survive. The sex urge, for example, assures the propagation of the human race. It also enables us to attain biological immortality. Sex and love become intermingled. They represent aspects of the same instinct of survival, making life enjoyable for us and giving meaning to life. Fear is another facet of self-preservation. It keeps us cautious and aware of the hazards of life.

• Hate in Relation to Fear

We can never hope to *understand* and *control hate* until we learn to *understand* and *control fear.* People hate because they feel *insecure.* The person who is most apt to hate is one who harbors feelings of inferiority. He is frustrated, anxious, suspicious, and fearful. People who hate are going through life with *clenched fists.* They are constantly on the defensive. More than likely they have been exposed to patterns of hatred during childhood. They are *conditioned* to hate and in many instances are merely *imitating* the hate-reactions of their parents.

People hate because they have been deprived and are still being deprived of the love they wanted and the love they need. They feel *rejected.* They harbor the sad delusion that to survive they must hate. They are encouraged in their convictions by the cynical philosophy that it is a "dog-eat-dog" world—that everyone is selfish and dishonest and that the only way to get ahead in this world is to keep fighting and out-hating their fellow man. For them life becomes a vicious cycle of insecurity leading to hate and hate resulting in more in-security. Every day becomes a competitive struggle for sur-vival. Surviving, no matter how, becomes an obsession. They realize the tragedy of their faulty reasoning when their cynical philosophy of life backfires. They unfortunately learn through sad experience that hate begets hate, that revenge and vin-dictiveness are futile.

War for instance is the end-result of epidemics of hate. Even nations are finally awakening to the cold realization that there is no victory in any war.

To summarize, *people* hate because of fear. They fear death, God, people, and the greatest of all their fears—the fear of fear itself.

● Consequences of Self-Hatred

Hatred is a *negative* emotion. Any negative emotion is capable of making one *sick*. Hate induces anger, which in turn may lead to a crime of passion. Hate is *habit-forming*. Riots are often incited by hate. The hate of the individual becomes the hate of society. When we hate ourselves, we hate others. When others hate us, we in turn hate them. Hating others is accompanied by unconscious if not conscious feelings of guilt that lead to self-hatred.

● Hate Produces Health Complications

Self-hatred is capable of producing serious health complica-tions. The man who always flies into a rage when anything upsets him is apt to succumb to a cerebral accident. A person suffering from high blood pressure surely doesn't benefit from spells of anger. Hate is an ulcer-producing emotion, can cause headaches and nervous skin rashes, can take away your ap-petite, keep you awake at night, cause your marriage to fail, jeopardize your job, and alienate you from your fellow man. Hate makes you *tense*. Love makes you *relax*.

• *It Is* Abnormal *to Hate*

Many people who consult a psychiatrist often prove to be difficult patients only because they are saturated with feelings of personal unworthiness and pent-up feelings of *hostility.* They have a chip on their shoulder and are mad because of having to pay for the psychiatric treatment of a condition that they are prone to blame on others. They do not like to be told that their problems of unhappiness are self-induced.

When the psychiatrist exerts an effort to be kind and understanding, the neurotic patient, filled with bitterness and hate, often becomes abusive. He is unable to accept the kindness and the love that the psychiatrist radiates. It makes him feel more guilty. I have had patients who told me that they could not stand to have anyone be kind to them. It either made them hostile or it made them cry. When the psychiatrist is firm the patient misinterprets the firmness for *rejection.* He becomes suspicious and, as a consequence, becomes defensively abusive. The psychiatrist becomes the target for the antipathy his patient has developed over the years toward his parents.

Every psychoanalyst experiences this mechanism of *loving* and *hating* among his patients. When the patient begins to develop faith in the treatment (*positive transference*) directed toward the development of *normal self-love,* he soon begins to shed his outer hard shell of defensiveness and realizes for the first time that hating has gotten him nowhere. His health improves as his attitudes change. He finally becomes convinced that hate has been a costly handicap.

• *The Man Who Hated Women*

One young man was referred to me by his physician because his stomach ulcer had failed to heal with diet and medication. He hated women and boasted that he was always able to force women into submission—that women responded better to men who were forceful and who dominated them with an iron hand. He ridiculed the idea of marriage and cynically stated that love was something manufactured in Hollywood.

He had made a career of hating and abusing women, subjecting them to a master-slave relationship. He enjoyed
bullying them into submission. The normal woman never
went out with him a second time. He only appealed to women
who were decidedly neurotic—who sought an outlet for their
masochistic tendencies.

A psychological study of his background revealed a long
standing hatred of his mother. He felt rejected by her since
early childhood. Following his father's death, his mother
remarried. His stepfather was an alcoholic. He never knew
what it felt like to be loved by a woman. His bitterness increased with years. He hated himself, everyone and everything. His ulcer was the price he paid for his hatred.

I tried to convince him that one cannot hate others without hating oneself; that you cannot hate yourself without
hating others. I tried to show him that with so much hostility
stored up over the years he couldn't expect to earn the love
of any woman, that a man who hates as much as he did was
ineligible for marriage.

Psychotherapy enabled him to dissipate his self-hatred and
hatred of women. He finally agreed that his primitive hatred
of women in general was motivated by an unconscious desire
to punish his mother for rejecting him.

• *How to Conquer the Impulse to Hate*

Some general principles about hate feelings and how to
conquer them may be summarized as follows:

1. Accept the fact that hate is a *disease,* that it is
   an early *habit-formation,* that it is *contagious,*
   and that it is capable of causing you to become
   physically and *mentally* ill.
2. Stop *disappointing* yourself. Don't deliberately
   do things that will cause you to feel guilty. Exag-
   gerating your deficiencies and feeling inferior
   without doing anything about it will only make
   you dislike yourself that much more. Hate is
   the poorest excuse for adjusting to any difficulty.

3. Develop *normal self-love*. Self-esteem and normal pride are essential to survival. Self-love, free of neurotic selfishness, is *medicine*. It is a *cure-all*.

4. Don't allow hate to displace love in your heart.

5. Akin to a fire-proof building, you can develop a *hate-proof soul*.

6. Don't return abusiveness with abusiveness. Tell yourself that people who hate are *sick*. Try to *teach* the person who hates that it is better to to love than to hate.

7. Suicide is a combination of *self-pity* and *self-hatred*.

8. When you are moved by the trigger impulse to hate, give yourself time to study the immediate situation before you say anything or act impulsively. Seek the better way of handling what appears to be an acute frustration. Don't say or do anything that you will regret later.

9. Don't let someone else's hate feelings rub off on you. Become immune to people who exhibit an *acid disposition* toward everything.

10. *Be kind to yourself*. Reward yourself when you have earned a pat-on-the-back.

11. It is a scientific fact and not a theory, that hate is the surface expression of some inner *fear*.

12. When you stop hating yourself and others you have contributed more than your share toward freeing the world of hate. The hate of the world is merely the projection of the hate of the individual, and the world is made up of individuals like you and I, your neighbor and your neighbor's neighbor. As individuals we are all susceptible to reactions of hate. Therefore it is our moral obligation to teach ourselves and others that it is *wiser to love than to hate*.

Session 18.

▰▰▰

It's Human to Have Troubles

● *We All Have Our Ups and Downs*

All of us have troublesome problems—*emotional ups* and *downs*—caused by life's disappointments, money-problems, job worries, family dissensions, marital difficulties, and a host of other types of frustrations. Rich or poor, troubles come to all of us. Life is very unpredictable. No one knows with certainty from one day to the next just what the next day will bring. The fact that no one can feel completely *secure* in anything subjects us all to a *common* frustration. We are all in the same boat trying to make the most of life, adapting ourselves to each changing situation.

● *It Is Our Duty to Survive Life's Frustrations*

While it may be true that many of us bring on our own misfortunes it is also true that many of us often become the innocent victims of Fate. A death in the family is an example of a common major frustration. Death is likely to knock at anyone's door. Assuming the philosophical attitude that anyone at any time can suddenly be confronted with a serious problem because of unforseen circumstances makes us realize no one is exempt from life's frustrations. We can only be held responsible for those troubles that we have deliberately

192

brought on ourselves, due to faulty judgment or some other reason. While we are all capable of making serious mistakes, the important thing is to profit from our sad experiences.

We cannot always zig-zag away from life's difficulties. When troubles come to us it is only natural that we should have our moods of depression and discouragement. It's only *human* to find ourselves occasionally in difficulty and reacting to it with temporary despondency. We are inclined to ask: "Why did this have to happen to me? Why couldn't it have happened to someone else instead?" Nevertheless, to remain *continually* depressed because of some major frustration is an emotional reaction that is *unhealthy* and capable of making you *sicker* than you'd ever want to be.

• *Are You a Chronic Worrier?*

Everyone worries about anything and everything, if by worrying we mean being concerned. It is the quality and quantity of our worrying that determines whether we are normal or neurotic. Worry as used in the popular sense, however, generally refers to an *abnormal* concern over some existing frustration, something that happened in the past about which we feel guilty or something unpleasant we fear may happen to us or others.

Worry (thinking in a circle) is frequently at the root of unrelieved depression and unhappiness. It is an attention-getting mechanism. A chronic worrier *dissipates* his energy only because the things he worries about seldom happen. As a clergyman, Dr. Lloyd Foster, aptly expressed it: "To worry is as foolish and wasteful as driving one's car into the garage and leaving the motor running all night. A tremendous amount of energy would be consumed, but the car would not be going anywhere." Worry means making your mind *work* 24 hours a day.

• *Give Yourself This Worry Test*

The following test should enable you to gain some inkling as to whether or not you fit in the above category of a chronic worrier. Ask yourself the following questions. Check the "yes" or "no" column. If the majority of your checks are "yes" answers, you no doubt have the personality of a neurotic worrier.

		Yes	*No*
1.	Do you bring your work troubles home and lie awake thinking about them?	———	———
2.	Are you constantly preoccupied with health-complaints?	———	———
3.	Does the least emotional stress give you a feeling of butterflies in your stomach?	———	———
4.	Do you go from doctor to doctor trying to find out what's wrong with you?	———	———
5.	Are you overly cautious about everything?	———	———
6.	Do you take a pessimistic view of most things?	———	———
7.	Are you inclined to make mountains out of molehills?	———	———
8.	Are you overconcerned about what other people think?	———	———
9.	Are you continually worried about the welfare of members of your family?	———	———
10.	Do you dwell on past mistakes?	———	———
11.	Do you worry about going insane, dying, developing cancer?	———	———
12.	Do you lack confidence in the future?	———	———
13.	Are you superstitious?	———	———
14.	Do you worry about God punishing you?	———	———
15.	Are you a perfectionist?	———	———
16.	Were you brought up by parents who worried to excess?	———	———
17.	Have you always been serious-minded?	———	———
18.	Are you oversensitive to criticism, easily offended, and addicted to brooding over slights?	———	———
19.	Can you trace your worry-habit to some painful frustration in the past?	———	———

20. Do you worry about everyday respon-
    sibilities?   _____ _____
21. Do you worry about the kind of impres-
    sion you make on other people?   _____ _____
22. Do you constantly talk about the things
    that worry you to those around you?   _____ _____
23. Must you be constantly reassured that
    nothing will happen to you?   _____ _____
24. Are you dependent on others to solve
    your troubles?   _____ _____
25. Do you worry excessively about other
    people's troubles and misfortunes?   _____ _____
26. Are your imagined fears associated with
    something you have read or heard?   _____ _____
27. Are you overly suspicious and doubt the
    integrity of your friends?   _____ _____
28. Are money-problems a constant source
    of worry?   _____ _____
29. Do you have a compulsive *need* to
    worry?   _____ _____
30. Are you the type to bite off more than
    you can chew and then worry about it?   _____ _____
31. Do you lack a sense of humor?   _____ _____
32. Are you afraid to enjoy life?   _____ _____

• The Frustration of Being Lonely

Many persons who are lonely are bitter and unhappy. They
have a sour attitude toward life. Instead of probing the *cause*
of their loneliness, they argue that people are *unfriendly.* An
unmarried girl may rationalize that there's no use going out
on dates because most men are "wolves." Others conclude
that the men they meet are either too young, too old, or
already married. Many widows because of feelings of self-
pity think that they do not fit in with groups of married
people.

Loneliness is a *symptom* rather than a condition. Anyone
can feel lonely—married or unmarried, alone or in a crowd.
Most lonely people lack imagination. Other than supporting
themselves by working, they do not know how to make the

most of their leisure time. They lack the ability to make friends. Actually there is no reason why anyone should feel alone and friendless. It is a matter of knowing how to establish companionships, how to make yourself interesting to others.

• *Loneliness Is Self-Induced*

Charles B. Roth, a writer of popular articles, described a woman, a widow of independent means, who lived in a family hotel where widowers and bachelors of her own age lived. She was lonely but repelled every attempt to make friends. After she had eaten she would shut herself up in her room, thinking that her fellow-lodgers were not good enough to associate with her.

There are many such people who will not put themselves out to make new acquaintances and cultivate friendships with others. To combat loneliness you must start out with the right attitude about people. You must assume that there are many others besides yourself who are also lonely and are seeking new friendships. But to gain friends you must start by *being* one.

The person who is lonely is apt to feel inferior and thinks that others are not interested in him. Others are tactless and exhibit in the presence of strangers their personality-shortcomings, prejudices, and hatreds; or they discuss their health-complaints and in this way make themselves unattractive. This fault can be easily remedied. It merely takes a bit of effort to make yourself pleasant to others and analyze what you are about to say before saying the wrong thing at the wrong time. You cannot hope *not to be lonely* if you dislike people and stay away from them. Refusing invitations to go places becomes a *habit*, and after awhile you almost prefer to be lonely than to exert enough effort to attend functions where you can meet and make new friends. Living in an ivory tower adds to your loneliness. Choose the right places to go for the quality of friends you are seeking. When you meet new people get to know them better.

• Advice to the Lonely

Lonely people need to find something constructive to occupy their evenings and week-ends. There are a thousand-and-one things a person can do of an absorbing nature. A lazy person can never find anything that interests him. A common hobby brings many people together and is a means of establishing new friendships. There are clubs you can join where you can participate in social activities.

Before setting out to make new friends, analyze your personality. Correct any serious defects you may have. You can't be snobbish, standoffish, or antagonistic and expect people to like you. No one likes a person with an ugly disposition. If you are conscious of your faults, feeling sorry for yourself doesn't help. *Remedy them.*

Doing things for others is a quck way of gaining friends. Giving others a feeling of self-importance makes you attractive to them. You can never hope to make friends as long as you try to find something wrong with each new person you meet. Everyone has quirks. You must learn to be tolerant and realize that no one is perfect. If you are unhappy, don't let the world know about it. If you meet unhappy people, don't run away from them. Try to help them and influence them toward improving their attitude toward life.

One of the greatest assets to develop in protecting yourself against being lonely is *self-sufficiency. Learn to live with yourself.* If you cannot make *yourself* happy, how can you make anyone else happy? Whenever a person tells you he *dislikes people* you can almost rest assured that he *dislikes himself.*

Stop brooding about loneliness. Through intelligent planning, logic, and common sense, anyone can overcome loneliness, irrespective of age or situation in life. *Make yourself your first friend, and others will follow.*

• Frustrations Need Not Overpower You

A young man in his late twenties brought me, in writing,

some miscellaneous thoughts about himself entitled "Random Thoughts," in which he described what he considered to be his "emotional problem."

> One of my worst defects is my disposition. I tend to be irritable, easily frustrated, and moody. For years, I was a perfectionist—quick to see error in things and people, including myself. As I grew into my late twenties, I became even more critical of the foibles, errors, chaotic organization, and inefficiency of the world at large, lamenting its hypocrisy and stupidity, and feeling that if only man would use his head, he could remedy all of it. This caused me to become sour in personality and soul, and I spent all my time worrying about major problems of the world instead of trying to develop my own immediate interests to the maximum.

As evidence that he finally learned to overcome his sensivity and irritability and no longer allowing himself to be chronically frustrated, he later wrote:

> In the past couple of years I have gradually undergone a fundamental change in outlook and personality, and the process is still going on. Not only have I fairly well overcome the anxiety and tension which was my original complaint, but the underlying emotions and frustrations causing this trouble have been altered. I am beginning to express my individuality with less reserve. I always had a what-makes-Sammy-run type of ambition—working, studying, and driving myself to prove myself worthy. Now I see the foolishness of this, realizing the importance of *living*, enjoying friends and everything good in life. Ambition I still have, but of a more healthy type, designed to help me achieve success and happiness without regard to making a lasting impression upon the world. I want to do my bit to improve the world, but not frustrate myself in a neurotic drive for fame at the expense of happiness, love, and wise living.
>
> I have learned to stabilize my emotional responses to a considerable degree, reducing the frequency of anger, depression, sorrow, envy, hate, and the like. I have taught myself not to be oversensitive to criticism, and I am less critical myself. As a conse-

quence I experience less frustration, and I find it
easier to get along with other people.

● *Self Acquired Insight*

Much of his success in bringing about a change in his
former attitudes can be attributed to the development of insight into the source of his early frustrations.

Much of my reformist zeal, I am sure, stemmed
from an acute sensitivity resulting from strife between my parents in my youth. Wanting to be a
champion of the underdog developed from an acute
inferiority complex starting in early life. I was too
extreme and too radical. My resentment against the
established order can probably be traced to my dislike of my father, which now has been dissipated.

I feel I have reached a state of inner tranquility.
I do not overconcern myself with things that are not
important. I look for the good in people and have
discovered that I become less irritated by anything
they say or do.

I recognize that my utterly ridiculous and impossible ideas about changing the world overnight are in
large part attributable to my childhood frustrations.
Now, I can enjoy the world, live in it and with it,
and not feel anxious because we cannot make it
Heaven tomorrow. It has made me more tolerant of
people and things and ideas. It has let me begin to
enjoy myself and relax at times, instead of thinking
I should be doing something constructive for the
world at all times. I recognize that a balanced life of
work and play is essential. I am more satisfied with
my accomplishments and very confident, although
not cockily so, that I can and will lead a successful
life in an attainable and realistic sense and not as a
new savior of the world, as I used to think of myself.

My psychosomatic symptoms have been on the
wane. No longer the fogginess, dizziness, splitting
headaches, pains in the groin, muscle spasms, gloomi-
ness, constant feelings of tension, and throat con-
striction. Once in a great while I experience a tight-
ness in my throat, difficulty in swallowing, and an occasional feeling of anxiety with slight headache, but
the severity is much reduced. I feel I have put much
of what I have learned to work.

There are many such individuals who develop emotional disorders because they *allow* themselves to become victims of everyday frustrations. They struggle from day to day in their unhappy state, never having learned how to cope with problem-situations intelligently.

• How to Manage Your Day-to-Day Frustrations

1. Convince yourself that every *situational-problem* has a proper *solution*. It is a matter of being patient and finding the right answer to your specific situation. This takes study and planning.

2. *Think* before you *act*. People are easily frustrated because they *allow* themselves to become emotionally upset. They do not give themselves a chance to calm down and become objective. They act impulsively and regret their action afterwards.

3. *Simplify* your life. Do not deliberately invite complications that will cause anxiety and worry.

4. When things go wrong think of something to *smile* or *laugh* about. Use your sense of humor when you need it most.

5. We can't always please everyone. To run into people who dislike us, is to be expected. Accept rejection stoically.

6. Sell yourself the idea that you have a *power within you* that will help you to meet adversities courageously—that will enable you to overcome most any obstacle.

7. Talk your problems out with someone you think can help you.

8. Handling your everyday frustrations *successfully* depends on how well you learn to control and master your emotions.

9. Don't be a *perfectionist*. Perfectionists are inclined to be easily frustrated because they expect too much of themselves and others. They are too *idealistic* and less realistic.

10. Before blaming others for your frustrations ask yourself, "Am I easy to live with?"

11. Instead of becoming upset because of not being able to make decisions, find out the causes of your indecisions.

12. Analyze the basic psychology of your frustrations. Persons who are *easily frustrated* are usually people who are *over-aggressive* and feel insecure and impatient.

13. Counterbalance your frustrations by rewarding yourself with activities that relax you.

14. Intelligent action is better than needless worry.

15. A change of routine can dispel the frustration of being bored with "the same old grind."

16. You can't solve your frustrations by turning your back upon them or by resorting to alcohol which merely *multiplies* frustrations. Frustration-drinking is always accompanied by an aftermath of guilt and more frustration.

17. When you are frustrated because someone has disappointed you, tell yourself that in reality no one disappoints anyone. People disappoint themselves.

▄▀

Learn to Forgive Yourself

- ## *It is Abnormal to be Unhappy*

Unhappiness is an *illness*. It is a form of self-poisoning of the mind. Let us treat it, then, as an illness—as something with a definite *cure*, well within our reach.

The humdrum routine of living—eating, sleeping, and working—is one of the most prevalent causes of boredom and unhappiness.

Many unhappy people are *drifters* on the sea of life, sailing their ship without a compass.

A young man, complaining of restlessness, boredom, frequent headaches, emotional instability, and general nervousness, entered a southern university. All during his freshman year, he could not make up his mind about what he wanted to be or what studies to pursue at college. He finally left school, spent the next six months in idleness and then persuaded an uncle to give him a desk job. After three months, he became bored and decided to travel. Upon his return he began to manifest a host of neurotic symptoms for which he sought psychiatric help.

Another drifter? Well, not too far. Under professional care

202

this foot-loose individual adapted a program organized to fit his requirements. His cooperation and adherence to a set of plans netted him the reward of a happy social and economic adjustment.

● *Are You Responsible for Your Own Unhappiness?*

There are many *self-induced causes* of unhappiness—a shirking of life's responsibilities, loss of self-confidence, exaggerated fears and worries, greed, "wanting" instead of "giving," a joyless monotonous type of existence, feelings of unworthiness and self-condemnation, sympathy-seeking habits, emotional immaturity, loneliness, feelings of persecution, and hatred.

● *Unhappiness Is an Attitude of the Mind*

There are two kinds of emotional reactions to personal misfortune. (1) *Normal* and (2) *Abnormal.* If one becomes depressed following a sorrowful event and the reaction is a temporary one, we consider the individual *normal.* However, when the person refuses to make an adjustment to sorrow and remains chronically unhappy, the reaction is abnormal.

I have been asked many times, "What would make a person continue to be unhappy?"

Feeling sorry for oneself is a cause of chronic unhappiness. It is a form of attention getting, a desire to have the world express a sympathetic wish to share our unhappiness.

● *Neurotics Verbalize and Advertise Their Unhappiness*

Neurotics keep *reminding* themselves of their great misfortune. They hug their grief to their breast for fear they will forget. They enjoy telling all their friends about their troubles. They want to share their unhappiness with anyone who will listen, for unhappiness is contagious.

Emotionally mature individuals do not advertise the heavy pain they feel in their heart. They make every attempt to survive the psychological effects of a personal tragedy. The neurotic achieves vicarious satisfaction in the importance he creates by enlisting the attention and sympathy of his friends. He enjoys the attention his unhappiness attracts. He wears the expression of a troubled mind.

If you were to suddenly come upon a woman standing in a corner weeping you would be inclined to ask her if there is anything you could do to help. Literally, there are many such persons weeping, without visible evidence of tears; their "crying" is disguised in their complaint of unhappiness. Like a victrola needle caught in the groove of a worn-out record, they repeat over and over the details of some past misfortune.

The innocent bestowal of sympathy and pity upon a person who forever voices his unhappiness is harmful. Being severe or indifferent is equally injurious. No one likes to be called a neurotic or to be scolded for something he does not understand and thinks he cannot help.

It takes patience and ability to re-educate such a victim to a point wherein the psychology of his unhappiness becomes apparent to him. The hidden motivations of his morbid state of mind must be brought to a level of conscious understanding.

• *Unhappiness in Adulthood Often Stems from Unhappiness in Childhood*

Another reason why some react in an abnormal way to the everyday misfortunes of life, is that unhappiness is not only contagious and often motivated by self-pity, but it is also the result of conditioning in early life. By this is meant that unhappy adults as a rule were unhappy children and, more than likely, came from unhappy homes. Continually exposed to the unhappiness of their parents, they become addicted to reactions of unpleasantness in a neurotic way. They imitated their parents for so many years that they forgot how to react in any other fashion. They become slaves to the habit of being unhappy.

There is a risk in marrying someone who is unhappy or who comes from an unhappy home. The tendency is to carry over the unhappiness of childhood into married life. Young people who suffer from chronic unhappiness should not look forward to marriage as a solution to their many problems. Unhappiness is a psychological illness that should be successfully treated prior to the wedding ceremony. Unhappiness, therefore, is *habit-forming,* stemming from frustrations rooted in a miserable childhood.

● A Need for Atonement

This brings us to another important factor—one that helps to explain the high incidence of neurotic unhappiness—namely, self-induced guilt associated with an unwillingness to forgive yourself and a need for atonement—*masochism*—a complex whereby the individual indulges in self-torment.

You may have heard someone state that certain persons are "never happy unless they are unhappy." It is equivalent to the contradiction of witnessing a mother cry at her daughter's wedding and remarking: "I'm crying because I'm so happy for her." The same holds true for neurotics who *find* reason to be unhappy. They dig out of the past something for which they feel *guilty* and then proceed to spend the rest of their life *atoning* for it. They revive the incident that brings on the feelings of guilt subconsciously in order to have something to punish themselves for.

Loretta was a young girl who had left home because she could not get along with others of her family, none of whom "understood" her. She was lonesome, living in a strange city, and began to drink to help fight off the urge to return home. Following her addiction to alcohol, she became promiscuous and was shocked one day to discover that she was pregnant. She took poison in an effort to escape it all. Her landlady, suspecting something, entered her room and found her prostrated on the floor. She was rushed to the nearest hospital where she had a miscarriage as a result of the excessive vomiting but soon recovered. This all happened several years prior to seeking psychiatric help. Following this episode she became carefree, continued to drink, and once again threatened to take her life. It was obvious that she was trying to punish herself for the guilt she experienced as a result of her many escapades. Many of the twenty-two thousand suicides that occur every year in the United States are perpetrated by guilt and feelings of self-contempt.

• Afraid to Be Happy

There are great numbers of persons who feel they are not *deserving* of happiness. Some are even superstitious about it. They feel that if they show any sign of happiness some ill will befall them. Such individuals are *afraid* to be happy.

The people who come under this category actually go out looking for trouble. When it comes, it satisfies an unconscious wish: they now have something to repent. The normal person is capable of making mistakes accompanied by distressing results, but in seeking forgiveness he also forgives himself. He profits from his experience and avoids making the same mistake again. The neurotic becomes enmeshed in one misfortune after another. Psychoanalysts claim that neurotics, those who admit their unhappiness, gain erotic satisfaction from this *need to suffer*. Their unhappiness is a self-inflicted atonement for the sins of the past.

• Don't Make Unhappiness Your Alibi

An unhappy person is likely to use his unhappiness as an alibi for his failures—his sense of inadequacy, his inability to assume responsibility. He attributes all of his difficulties to the fact that he was a victim of hard luck. It's a good way of kidding himself—like winning at solitaire by dealing from the bottom of the deck. It's the laziest way out of not working for the things that bring happiness.

These people use the misfortunes of the past to explain why they are in a rut. They resort to "ifs" and "buts" whenever someone suggests a remedy for their present predicament.

• What to Tell Yourself if You're Unhappy

1. Unhappiness is an illness of the mind.

2. It is contagious.
3. *Forget* to be unhappy. It can become a habit and an obsession.
4. Recognize the motivations behind your unhappiness if you want *not to be unhappy*.
5. Realize that troubles come to all of us. It is not what happens to you but your reaction to it that determine whether you will be temporarily unhappy or suffer chronic neurotic unhappiness.
6. Make yourself too busy to be unhappy. Devote your energy toward being kind to others. Kindness has its own reward. Even Buddha must have known this for he said: "To do a little good is more than to accomplish great conquests." He advocated *friendliness* as a means of release from unhappiness and fear, defining friendliness as "affection unsullied by hope or thought of any reward on earth or in heaven." Buddha's philosophy maintains that "Friendship is the only cure for hatred, the only guarantee of peace."
7. Don't live in the past. Your past is like a meal previously consumed.
8. If it has to be a grouch or a smile, choose smiling. The grouch will fade away. The response to your smile will make you glad *inside* and that's where *happiness* starts; just there—*inside*.

*S*ession 20.

▗▖

Grow Wiser as You
Grow Older

● *You Are as Old as You Feel*

The familiar saying that a man is as old as he *feels* is truly far more than a popular catch phrase. In it are the seeds of *wisdom*. Old age must first exist in the *mind* before it becomes a *reality*.

After crossing the equatorial age of our lives, most of us have a tendency to react in one of two ways. Either we yield, as if under the power of a magnet, to the forces of growing old, or we challenge our approaching years courageously, striving to maintain our zest for life.

The mere fact that you are forty, or fifty, or sixty years of age is of relatively little import. It doesn't mean much. The important question is: What is your *real* age? Just how old are you, anyway? You are more likely to find the true answer in your *mind*.

How true are these words of George Sokolsky, on the theme of enduring youth:

208

Each of us is ambitious to remain everlastingly youthful, to dance gaily at sixty; to be interested in all of life at seventy; to keep one's wits at eighty. And why not? Years are the artificialities of the calendar makers. If the spirit is young, the years are not even remembered. If the spirit remains young, one can sing a song of youth at eighty as at eighteen but at eighty it will have more meaning.

• Make Your Own Age

Each man, to a degree, makes his own age. I do not have reference solely to physical elements. Many and many a man has taken his setting-up exercises with unvarying regularity; has abjured alcoholic stimulants, limited himself to one after-dinner cigar—and yet grown old before his time. Why? Because the fear of age—the dread of advancing years—was forever gnawing at his heart, aging him day by day, even as he sought to forestall the inevitable.

Old age is nothing more or less than an unconditional surrender to the old man with the scythe. You make this surrender at forty, fifty, at sixty, at seventy—at *any* age. But you need not make it at all. Instead, if you will, you can journey through life as many a valiant traveler before you has done, jousting strong-heartedly with the years, marked but not marred by age.

We have clung rather tenaciously to the conviction that an ailing old age is inevitable. We speak pessimistically of the "declining years" and anticipate a doddering dotage almost as a matter of course. And to tell the truth, there has been no lack of evidence to support this point of view. Only the exceptionally favored individual has escaped the hampering hand of disease.

• You Keep Young by Keeping Your Thoughts Young

The body will gradually age; the hair will turn gray and thin; the arteries will harden; the muscles will lose their resilience; and the skin will wrinkle and lose its bloom. This is inevitable, but we can keep the spirit young. We do not grow old mentally, except when we let our ideas solidify and block up the channels of appreciation. The mind matures, but it does not age like other organs; or at least the process of disintegration is so slow as to be indiscernible in most people. Science has proved this fact.

We have said that we keep young by keeping our thoughts young. By this we do not mean a return to the gaiety of youth or to youthful dress and play. Nothing is quite so ridiculous as an aged person aping the young, a parody of youth. What is meant is that if we keep up our interest in the progress of the world, if our education continues to grow, if we haven't lost our sense of humor, if we do not over-evaluate ourselves and our own ideas nor underevaluate others and their opinions, then we do not grow old.

• *There is no Need to Fear Our Advancing Years*

Age has been referred to as a mere tradition of past regrets, future fears, and day dreams of youthful conquests. Those who spiritually resign themselves to the ills and fears of middle life are merely making their neurotic tendencies their primary interest in life, with the dire consequence that they soon become self-centered introverts, obsessed with feelings of despondency and self-pity. They find themselves blind in their shadow of old age, physically decrepit at the fourth or fifth decade of life, victimized by a premature loss of youthful interests.

Isn't it, after all, rather foolish—and obviously foolish— to worry and shudder at the realization of having reached your fortieth year? Here at last you have attained the radiant age when you can feel free from the responsibilities of youth and *wiser* from the experiences accrued during manhood.

Men have always had a morbid tendency in the autumn of life to fear the later years. They begin to grow old physically when they should begin to live mentally.

Remember that we all still prefer to drink the wine that

has aged and to smoke the pipe that has mellowed. For melody the discerning musician choses an old violin. Why, then, should we hesitate to savor life at its seasoned best?

• The Harvest Years of Your Life

You should never grow old if you reap from day to day the harvest of life, forever seeking new interests to satisfy the hunger of an intellectual appetite.

In *Life Begins at Forty*, Walter Pitkin says:

> I shall argue that many millions of our citizens can get much more out of their fourth, fifth, and sixth decades of life than out of any of the first, simply by learning how to live and how to make the most of opportunities within reach. Further, I shall maintain that the more fortunate millions in the upper income classes can double or treble their enjoyment merely by mastering a modern philosophy of life.[1]

• Are You a Pessimist or an Optimist?

Past middle life we become either aimless pessimists or aggressive optimists. We all know the pessimists. Indeed, we probably know far too many of them. The pessimist is the crepe-hanger, the joy-killer, the human tombstone. The far-sighted optimist on the other hand—the proprietor of a million dollar disposition—loves life, seldom complains of his sorrows, and is always reflecting a spirit of youth.

• Just Beginning to Live

I remember the case of a happily married college professor who had been a serious-minded, hard-working scholar practically all of his life. He exhibited very little interest in recreational pleasures until he reached his forty-fifth year. At that stage of life, he became possessed of a sudden transformation of personality. He began to smoke, indulged in highballs, and attended dances frequently. His anxious wife requested a psychiatric explanation for this change of behavior. After

---

[1] Walter Pitkin, *Life Begins at Forty*. New York: Whittlesey House, 1932.

excluding every possibility of an illness, it was determined that our friend was merely indulging the luxuries of a youth he had never had. His own justification was that he had found himself and was just beginning to live.

This is an entirely human and, in some respects, even a commendable reaction. Such tardy awakening of the normal instinct for play have provided the plots of innumerable works of fiction. And we encounter examples rather frequently in real life.

• Some Professional Advice

It isn't difficult to understand the elation of a cloistered individual who stumbles suddenly upon a discovery that there is an awful lot of fun to be had in this old world of ours. Let it be understood that I'm all for this Awakened Man. Count me definitely on his side. But if I can get him off the dance floor and away from that tantalizing blonde, I want to whisper into his ear a *few words of timely counsel*. In my capacity as a psychiatrist I'd like to say something like this:

Mr. Van Winkle, I'm delighted to see that you are beginning to emerge from your forty years' nap. That's great. Rub the sleep out of your eyes and join the party. But—and I hope you'll lend an attentive ear to this point; its really pretty important —don't try to make up for lost time. It just can't be done.

There are certain pleasures and pastimes that are plainly labelled *For Youth Only*. Let them be; they aren't for you. Youngsters revel in them, and it's right and proper that they should. But with your background and experience, your mature viewpoint, you'll find no enduring satisfaction in "going adolescent." You will only wind up by missing the richer pleasures that await you in your own age group. Have fun. Have plenty of fun. But have forty-ish fun.

• Make Your Sunset Years Richer, Happier Ones

Arthur Christopher Benson points out that there are definite gains to make up for the loss of youth. For one thing,

he says, we persons of middle age have lost the self-consciousness of youth. We no longer expect to be impressive.
We say what we think, fully aware that our point of view is
but one of many, and quite prepared to revise it.

With age the tyranny of convention decreases.
Gradually I discovered that people troubled their
heads very little about what one did; that the "right"
people were often the most tiresome and that the
only games worth playing were the games which one
enjoys.

It is true that there were sharper ecstacies in
youth; keener perceptions and more passionate
thrills. But then the mind also dipped more swiftly
into discouragement, dreariness and despair. Life
is not so rapturous, but it is vastly more interesting
. . . in youth, mistakes seemed irreparable, calamities
intolerable, disappointments unbearable. I have
learned that mistakes often can be set right, that
calamities have sometimes a compensating joy, that
a disappointment is often of itself a rich incentive to
try again. One learns that hope is more unconquer-
able than grief. And many of the sorrows of life
lie in the imagination.[1]

The best way to cheat age is to learn to control our dis-
abling emotions for the maintenance of a happy mental disposition upon which youth largely depends.

Our goal is not merely a *longer* life, but a *richer, happier*
one. After all, there is not much point in lingering on in a
vale of tears and tribulations. Unless the later years can be
full of zest, interest, and meaning, they are scarcely worth
the effort required to keep the dull ember of life from ex-
tinguishing. Who cares to live unless he can *live?*

• How Old Are You?

Now that you're forty does old age seem just around the
corner? Are you developing a gray disposition with your
gray hair? When your doctor tells you he's found nothing

---

[1] Arthur Christopher Benson, *Where No Fear Was*. N. Y. and London, G. P.
Putnam's sons, 1914.

wrong with you physically, and still you know you don't feel quite up to par, stop worrying long enough to give yourself an age test. It might prove the root of your entire trouble. Give yourself a mental shake-up by asking such simple and revealing questions as these:

1. Are you becoming more frequently depressed, giving vent to feelings of self-pity? If so, why?
2. Are you constantly day-dreaming in the past?
3. Are you heart-conscious, fearing overexertion might bring on a fatal heart attack?
4. Does your wife have to bury her elbow in your ribs to keep you from falling asleep in the movies?
5. Have you cut your golf down to nine holes?
6. Have you lost that laughter in your eyes?
7. Do you go into a huddle because your children call you "old man"?
8. Are you too dependent and possessive?
9. Can you still appreciate a spicy story or get a kick out of a mildly salacious cartoon?
10. Do you associate with friends of your same age or do you mingle with the younger set?
11. Have you a tendency to lie when a young attractive woman wants to know how old you really are?
12. Do you worry over trivialities, and are you inclined to be pessimistic about most things?
13. Do you prefer spending most of your evenings at home?
14. Have you told your wife you'd rather sleep in twin beds now that you're getting up in years?
15. Are you easily irritated, unduly sensitive?
16. Are you becoming more intolerant, critical, and domineering?
17. Do you envy young people?
18. Are your health-complaints excessive?
19. Are you bored with life?
20. Are you too lazy to take up an absorbing hobby?
21. Are you developing a sour disposition?

22. Do you have an open mind about other people's way of living?
23. Have you stopped going to church?
24. Is gossiping a pastime with you?
25. Do you feel that you are too old to change?
26. Do you reject advice from those younger than you are?

• Can Overwork Cause Premature Aging?

We hear quite frequently, the assertion that a certain individual is "working himself to death." There may, perhaps be some truth in the observation, but as a rule, I am moderately skeptical. True, very hard physical labor, under adverse conditions may age a man prematurely; may, indeed, kill the weakling before he becomes inured to his tasks. But in the sedentary occupations followed by most of us, the danger of overwork is rather remote.

Upon closer examination you will find that it is not overwork that is aging the burdened executive, but the cares and worries of high office, which he has not learned to cast off. And not infrequently you will find, as an added complication, an unsatisfactory domestic relation. Work had nothing to do with those deep-etched furrows in the brow. Worry stamped them there. Worry during the autumn season of your life is a grindstone that wears down your span of life.

• An Example of Youth Triumphant

Few of us realize, perhaps, that Benjamin Franklin was in his seventy-first year when he set out for Paris to undertake the delicate diplomatic task of negotiating an alliance between France and the United States. Most of his contemporaries had long been hovering in the chimney-corner, waiting resignedly, for the Grim Reaper. But Franklin, through his sparkling personality, gained a powerful ally for his country, and much distinction for himself. He was nearly 77 when he negotiated the treaty with Great Britain that made our country a republic. Within a few months of his eightieth birthday,

Franklin was elected governor of Pennsylvania, with but one dissenting vote; he was twice re-elected unanimously.

And bear in mind, that Franklin was eighty-one years old when he again demonstrated his unimpaired mental faculties at the convention that framed the Constitution of the United States. Youngsters half his age fell to squabbling amongst themselves on the issue of representation by states or by population. It was Franklin who smoothed the situation by suggesting the device of the Senate, which, in effect, achieved representation both by states and by population. Yes, a grand old man, indeed, by whatsoever standard you may elect to judge him.

• Famous People Never Grow Old

Going further back than Franklin's time, Michaelangelo continued to produce masterpieces at 89; *Faust* was completed by Goethe at the age of 81; and Tennyson was 83 when he wrote his "Crossing Of The Bar."

We find added inspiration in the contemporary lives of such persons as Dwight D. Eisenhower who was elected to the highest office in the country while in his 60's; the retired President Harry Truman (in his 70's) who decided to travel; Mrs. Eleanor Roosevelt, Winston Churchill, Presidential Advisor Bernard Baruch, Nobel Prize winner Selman Waksman, Carl Sandburg, Helen Keller, Ethel Barrymore, and artist Grandma Moses.

• Slow Down But Don't Retire

Retired business and professional men, in unnumbered thousands today find themselves restless and chafing under the bonds of inactivity. They seek desperately for something —anything—to fill the empty hours of their monotonous days. Indeed, the problem has assumed such serious proportions that several of the large insurance companies have taken cognizance of it. When a healthy, active man (regardless of age) retires abruptly from a business in which he has been a driving force, the insurance actuary gravely shakes his head, and begins to do sums in subtraction. Cold statistics show that such action will usually shorten a man's days on this old earth. His insurance company would much rather see him taper off gradually, delegate a little more authority to subordinates, acquire a few outside interests, and still keep sufficiently close to the business so that his intellect may be whetted on the grindstone of daily activities. In other words, their counsel is: *Slow down, but don't retire.*

There is a queer quirk in human nature that leads most of us to the boastful conclusion, that, while we may have our short-comings we can handle two things well: our liquor and our leisure. Too often we are wrong on both counts. Most of us, I suppose, have thought at one time or another of retiring. The business or professional man of middle years rather looks forward to the time when he can "take things easy"; when he will no longer be impelled by industry or compelled by necessity to maintain the frantic pace. Yes, he thinks of this time, regards the prospect longingly. But he makes no intelligent plans to fill his future years.

• Have You Made Plans for Your Leisure Years?

The next time a friend or associate speaks of retirement, try this experiment. Ask him point-blank what he intends to *do* with his leisure. Five will get you ten that he dismisses the subject with an airy assurance, "Oh, no trouble about *that.* I'll find plenty of things to do." And he is perfectly sincere about it. It seems to him now that the easiest thing imaginable would be to spend an endless succession of newly-minted days doing nothing in particular. He has never found leisure a pressing problem, because he has had so little of it. Vacations and holidays are crowded to the brim. Always more things to do than time to do them. His mind cannot well encompass the problems of a perpetual vacation.

But pursue the subject further. Insist that your friend catalog his proposed activities and you'll receive vague, evasive answers. "Oh, er, well, I'll travel a lot, of course. Get about and see the world. Something I've always wanted to do."

Natural enough. That seems to be the one universal yen. The more crowded our lives have been with routine the more we long to "get away from it all." And when we think of getting away, our minds usually take a geographical turn.

• So You're Going to Travel

I yield to no man in my enthusiasm for travel and in my belief that it is one of the most stimulating and satisfying of our recreational activities. But travel for pleasure is primarily a reaction. It's great to get away for a few weeks—a few months, even. Makes you appreciate home all the more.

But travel is no *occupation* for a healthy man who has fifteen or twenty good zestful years ahead of him. Not until you've visited foreign capitals and observed the harried and harassed tourists trotting doggedly and dutifully from castle to cathedral—not until you have actually experienced these things —can you realize what a confounded chore "cultural" travel can become. No more horrible fate could be wished on a man than the fate of being doomed to a decade of aimless travel, in the approved guidebook manner. No, keep travel to *spice* your days. You'll need something more substantial and more satisfying to fill the bulk of your time.

The simpler but rather obvious truth is that to retire successfully—avoiding, on the one hand, too much idleness and, on the other, a too strenuous avocation—is an art. It requires careful systematic planning, well in advance. In so important a life program you can hardly hope to stumble haphazardly onto happiness.

It is important to have a *plan*—one that meets your needs and desires—and then follow it conscientiously. Only in this way can you be sure of leading a truly satisfying life when, by necessity or inclination, you retire from your regular occupation.

• A Feeling of Being Useful and Needed

Dr. O. Spurgeon English, Philadelphia psychiatrist, claims

that the future of the older person lies to a large degree in his own hands.

He must develop so that he remains useful through his physical efforts or his personality qualities, or both, to the people of all ages around him. Then he will surely retain a word in the affairs of men. He will never be through, never feel superfluous, or never be without an outlet for the creative urge if he can do a job and make himself adaptable.

This implies that the older person need not retire to a life of complete leisure. He can make himself useful in one capacity or another so that he develops a feeling of being *needed*.

● *Secrets of Staying Young*

Growing *wiser* as you grow *older* means:

1. Reminding yourself that old age is what you make it—conceived in the mind—that you are never too old to *learn*. As Roger Bacon said: "Learning maketh a man fit company for himself." To learn is to know. To know is power. And power is the Captain of Youth.

2. *Wanting* to live longer, to increase your span of of life, you must live *intelligently*. You must live wholesomely; respect the laws of health and maintain an everlasting enthusiastic perspective on life.

3. *Slowing down*. It has been said morbidly that our lives are but marches to the grave. If the analysis of such pessimism be true, then why not learn to walk through life *slowly,* by taking shorter steps. Let him who chooses to run be the first to break the tape.

4. Remaining *young* in heart. You cannot control your *calendar* birthdays, but you can remain young in *mind* and *heart*. When I asked my mother-in-law who is eighty-seven, what the secret of her longevity was, she replied: "Frank, I guess it's because I like people. I've never

liked to be idle. Even at this age I am planning on having all new furniture in my living room. I get a thrill from traveling in an airplane. I enjoy going to church every Sunday. I think it's a wonderful world. There are so many wonderful things to see and do. I thank God for every day that I'm on this earth." There's the answer. With such a wise philosophy it is no wonder she is the grand, lovable person she is.

5. Forgetting past mistakes and disappointments, not allowing yourself to brood over *what might have been.*

6. Accepting your physical limitations graciously, growing old with dignity, complaining less, appreciating more, taking time out each day for mental and physical rest.

7. Taking stock of yourself, substituting undesirable traits common to so many old people with the cultivation of tolerance, understanding, kindness, and unselfishness.

8. Avoiding an over-inclination to worry about everything, letting your doctor worry about any health problems, placing greater faith in your Maker, and believing in yourself.

9. Finding greater enjoyment of life through new and exciting interests, taking a humorous view of things by learning to smile more and frown less.

10. Thinking of your birthdays as so many Thanksgivings, being thankful for each year. Growing older happily, getting a new lease on life, telling yourself "It's great to be alive." That you now have reached the age when you can live your own life depending upon the extent of your imagination and desires.

11. Mastering the art of living *gratefully.*

12. *Living* instead of just existing.

Session 21.

▰▰

The Power of Love

- ### *What Is Love?*

The word "love" is used a million times over in poems, songs, fiction; on stage, screen, radio, and television; and in daily conversation. Yet few of us stop to consider its true implication—what in the long run we really mean by love.

Some contend that there is no in-between about love. As the Southern preacher said: "You *is* or you *isn't* in love."

When I ask my patients for a definition of love, I never get the same answer twice. In most cases, they cannot even give me a clear idea of what love means to them.

I ask a wife, "Do you love your husband?"

The wife answers, "I don't know. I'm not sure."

"Did you love him when you married him, ten years ago?"

"I thought I did. But now I'm not sure whether I really loved him or not."

This wife is typical of thousands who are confused about their own emotions. They have never had a clear idea of what love really means, of whether or not the feeling they had for the man they married was love. What they called love could have been temporary love, physical attraction, a desire to escape from their own family, or it could have been a childish need to depend on someone.

When I ask husbands who are in a period of marital strife

221

if they love their wives, the answer is the same. They aren't
sure. They aren't sure they loved their wives to begin with.

I ask, "Can you tell me what you mean when you say you
love someone?"

"Love is just a feeling. It comes and goes. Sometimes you
have it, sometimes you don't. There's nothing you can do
about it. What is there to understand about love?"

• Things Everyone Should Understand About Love

Are you able to recognize the *real thing* and know when you
really love someone—and when they really love you?

The basic need for affection is so predominant in all of us
that the act of loving is unconsciously motivated by a wish
or need to be loved. A narcissistic element exists in every love
relationship. We demonstrate in a physical way what we like
the other person to do for us. Love at its best is *reciprocal.*

We are all born with the instinct to love, to enjoy the gift
of life. Love in its broadest sense is the love of life itself, of
living and surviving.

This kind of love is not dependent on people or circumstances outside of ourselves; it is an entity in itself. It is a
source of strength that makes physical pain endurable, mental
anguish tolerable.

A true love of life is the first prerequisite for the love between a man and a woman. When each has grasped the real
meaning of love, each has a good relationship to family,
friends, and associates.

Both are at peace with themselves, with their world and
God. They are not bedeviled by conflicts. Without this basic,
healthy love of life, romantic love is weak. After marriage,
petty quarrels, jealousies, money troubles, illness, every kind
of insecurity will set the partners to blaming each other. The
temporary attraction they believed was love breaks down
under the first real strain.

• Real Love Is Both Practical and Idealistic

In marriage, two people who have based their union on
real love are tolerant of each other's shortcomings. Real

love strives for the *ideal* relationship, because that is living at its best. But it is *practical* in allowing leeway for each other's faults.

Sometimes we are shocked to hear of the breakdown of a marriage that seemed perfect. "It's hard to understand. They were so much in love, they didn't even bother with anyone else. Neither ever took a step without the other."

The "ideal couple" were not really in love. They were neurotically clinging to each other. Each was dependent on the other to bolster up an uncertain ego, to shield against fear of life. The first hint that the partner is not living up to the ideal 100 per cent is an unbearable shock to the other. "How could this happen to me, to us?"

When two people know the real meaning of love, they do not rail at a partner for his failings. They do not sulk and turn their backs on a partner, because they do not turn their backs on life in general when it fails to live up to their ideals.

Real love is not possessive. As Dr. Harry Overstreet wrote: "The love of a person implies, not the possession of that person, but the affirmation of that person. It means granting him, gladly the full right to his unique humanhood. One does not truly love a person and yet seek to enslave him—by law or by bonds of dependence." [1]

Knowing the true meaning of love also safeguards us against abnormal self-sacrifice. Normal self-love is part of our love of life. It is normal to care about oneself enough to want to be well nourished, to feel well and look well, and enjoy what civilization offers in improved living.

Normal self-love is actually self-respect. Without it, a man or a woman becomes weak and masochistic, inviting martyrdom.

• *The Wrong Kind of Love*

A young woman, I shall call her Rosemary, is a living example of what the wrong kind of love can do to a life. When she came to me Rosemary was in her thirties, ill and nervous

---

[1] Dr. Harry Overstreet, *The Mature Mind*. (New York: W. W. Norton & Co., 1949).

and on the verge of suicide. She told me a long story of martyrdom at the hands of a husband who had mistreated her from the day they had married.

"I married when I was only seventeen. My parents didn't want me to marry Joe, but I loved him. After we married, even after our son was born, he drank and was brutal to me. Finally, it got so bad I had to separate from him.

"We stayed apart several years, then I went back and tried to live with him again. He was still cruel, and we separated again. Now my son is in his teens and I have tried living with my husband again, but he is worse to me than ever. I don't know what to do. I'm ready to commit suicide."

I asked her, "Why did you go back to your husband when he mistreated you?"

"I loved him. I still love him, no matter what he does. I can't help it."

"What about your son?"

"Oh, I love my boy, doctor. All those years away from my husband, I just lived for my son."

Rosemary wept. She was wallowing in a sea of false emotion.

I shocked her with the blunt truth. "You have never known the meaning of love. You don't love your husband. You are enjoying martyrdom at his hands. What you feel is *masochism*, not love. You are enjoying your own suffering. As far as your son is concerned, you don't love him either. If you did, you would be planning for his welfare. You would not be considering suicide as a way out, leaving him to cope with a brutal father. From the time you married at seventeen against your family's advice, you have been indulging in childish, heedless behavior. Love never entered into it."

This woman never had any real idea of the meaning of love. If she did, her whole life would have been lived differently.

And what of Rosemary's husband? What can a man have known about love if he abused his wife and neglected his child?

The answer is *nothing*. Like Rosemary, her husband never knew what love meant. He is an extreme example, but there are far too many men like him, to varying degrees, who have never had any concept of what the love between husband and wife should be.

• *A Rule of Nature*

In the married relationship between man and woman, there is a basic truth that both should keep in mind at all times: *Love in its practical, everyday aspect, means different things to a man and a woman.*

To a husband, love should be predominantly aggressive and protective. To a wife, love should be predominantly receptive. This is not a theory, but a rule of nature.

• *The Origin of All Love Is Maternal*

Modern man is in danger of forgetting that, although the male has the instinct to love, the instinct is stronger in woman because of her *maternal* role. Physically, emotionally, women are equipped by nature to give birth to life, to sustain and protect life. Men forget that this aspect of a woman's make-up affects her whole personality. Men forget that she is more sensitive, and has a greater capacity to love.

As children, we are all recipients of love and nourishment from the mother. It is mother who keeps us alive. Survival in infancy means that someone must love us enough to feed and protect us.

The majority of men are aware of the indebtedness to their mother for their life. They know that they were dependent on the mother as infants, and that she fed and loved and protected them. When the man is grown, he should make return for his gift of life by transferring love and protection to the woman he marries. Symbolically, in protecting his wife, he is returning the breast milk that gave him survival in infancy.

The normal man is aware that his role is one of *giving* love and protection to a woman.

● *"Eternal Sucklings"*

When a man seeks to reverse this role and becomes too passive and receptive in his relationship to a woman, he is neurotic. He wants from a woman in adult life the kind of coddling he received from his mother in infancy. Stekel calls such men "eternal sucklings". These men do not want a woman they will love and protect, they want a woman who will *give* them love.

Unfortunately, modern man is veering increasingly toward this upset in the role of male and female. It is fatal to masculine psychology. Clinical proof comes to me daily when men suffering from impotence and sex-failure blame it on their wives. They tell me, "I don't get enough love from my wife."

This catch phrase is common to our era. Universally men are heard to ask each other, "How much sex is she giving you? How much (love) are you getting from your wife?" It is equivalent to asking, "How much cradle rocking are you getting? Are you getting enough mother's milk and coddling?"

● *Adult Infantilism*

The impotence reaction in the male is a sign that he is oversensitive, childish. He has never made the transition to mature manhood and still regards himself as tenderly as if he were an infant. In relations with such a man, a wife has only to say the wrong thing, and he loses all desire at once. He is hurt, he sulks. He cannot carry out the role of husband toward her because he is too busy being the child.

Many men fall prey to this wrong thinking because our world is competitive. They have to work to support their families, and they feel they have done all that is required of them when they bring home the pay check.

It is true that man's primary function in life is to work, to achieve his ambitions, to be self-sustaining and earn the way for his family. But in order to carry out this main function, men need love and companionship during the competitive struggle.

● *Love and Companionship Need to Be Earned*

Husbands forget that love and companionship do not come
to anyone by divine right. These things have to be deserved.
A man does not get them by demanding, but by giving. The
man who strives to make his wife happy is well repaid; not
only does she try to make him happy, but the fruits of their
love are reflected in their home and their children.

There are, in my practice, an increasing number of neurotic
men who have a bargain concept of love—so much for so
much. They want full measure, and they watch suspiciously
to make sure they get it, like hagglers in the market.

Men who live by this attitude toward women are cheating
both their wives and themselves. They damage their own
capacity for love, and they kill spontaneous love from their
wives. They belong to the smug school of thought that makes
no effort to understand the psychology of love, much less the
psychology of women. "Women," they argue, "are an enigma.
They're to be *possessed*, not *understood*. There's no use trying to understand a woman."

Then they wonder why their sex relationships with their
wives are poor. I have shocked many of my men patients
by telling them, "In all your years of marriage, you have never
had a real love relationship with your wife. Your physical
relations with her represent nothing more than using her to
gratify your physical urge. You have never taken the trouble
to understand her or to win her response."

● *Sex Can Be a Gesture of Love*

The sex act between a man and a woman can represent
the ultimate expression of love. It is part of that parent love
that is the source of all our joy in life. As an expression of
love between a man and a woman, it renews and strengthens,
reawakens in both the awareness of the instinct to love, to
survive disaster together, and to enjoy their life for its own
sake.

I have often had married couples ask me, "Doctor, how

long does the sex relationship remain alive?" My answer to
this is that the sex relationship will remain alive just as long
as each maintains his or her love for the other. And while
emotion stays alive the fire never goes out on the hearthstone
of marriage. As Havelock Ellis once wrote: "Sex has a tendency to die in middle years only in couples who are un-
imaginative and where sex has become routine." In other
words, those couples who keep their sex life stimulated with
pleasant associations of planned and happy evenings, need
never fear divorce.

In the case of our couple, Rosemary and her husband, who
failed so badly in their marriage, they were only two out of
thousands of young people who are coping poorly with life
because their parents did not teach them the concept of real
love.

● *Children Need to Be Taught to Love*

Unless a child is taught, it cannot of itself understand the
meaning of real love and so have a citadel against the hurts
and frustrations it will meet in life.

What happens when a child receives its first fall, its first
cut? It screams protest. It is frightened. The small child
often asks, "Mother, will all the blood run out—will I die?"

The mother must teach him how to take this experience.
She dresses the cut, bandages and stops the bleeding. She
reassures the child that this is a common experience to us
all, that there will be a healing, and that he will not die.

What of his emotional hurts, later in life—the hurts to his
pride and his hopes, the threats to his security? The majority
of us, as children, have never been consciously taught to take
our cuts and bruises in the emotional field with courage. We
have not been taught to love life in the broad sense that will
enable us to bear personal injuries and losses with confidence
in the healing to come.

We do have one instinct that can become an enemy of love,
and that is fear. A baby will exhibit a natural joy in life, but
he will also show natural fear. When you clap your hands
sharply behind him, he tenses, he cries in fear.

As time goes on, if the baby is subject to many fears, if the
outside world inflicts too many shocks and hurts, his normal
love of self becomes a neurotic love of self. All his instinct
to love turns inward in self-protection. He grows up to be
neurotically selfish because he is frightened and insecure.

There are many ways in which a child's instinct to love can
be damaged. He may be physically handicapped or have
parents who treat him meanly or indifferently. He may have
someone he loves snatched from him by death.

• Consequences of Love-Insecurity

As a child matures to manhood, he has to face many disappointments and embittering failures. These things, inflicted
from the outside, make him first fearful, then resentful. Finally, his insecurity makes him suspicious and hostile toward
the whole world. He begins to hate everyone for what has
happened to him.

He may reject life so violently that he becomes alcoholic,
addicted to drugs, or criminal. He may even kill himself in
revenge on the world for its injustice.

The person who has been made neurotic by fear feels that
he has been especially selected to be hurt or disappointed.
Modern life produces many such people, because life is complex and competitive, and there are always threats to our
security.

Greater than any other threat is the damage to the love
instinct within. Neurotic selfishness is like a cancer to love.
It kills the very force in us that can heal and strengthen us
after fate deals a blow.

The true meaning of love implies the control of fear. To
gain the full power of love, each man must learn to estimate
the amount of insecurity life has subjected him to, without
despairing. He must remember that fear is universal, an instinct of self-preservation; but it is only protective when it
is *controlled*.

• How Grown-Up Are You About Love?

There are two kinds of love:

1. Normal or grown-up love
2. Neurotic or immature love

To be able to love you must grow up emotionally. Emotional immaturity is a barrier to normal love. You cannot expect to win respect and love if you are still tied to your mother's apron strings. That "silver cord" can sometimes extend from the womb to the tomb.

You need to have certain confidence in yourself before you are able to love.

• *What Is Your L. Q.?*

Ask yourself the following questions. The answers may give you some inkling as to your L.Q. (*Love-Quotient*) in relation to emotional immaturity.

1. Do you have a strong dependency on your parents?
2. What is your idea of love?
3. Do you feel insecure in your love relationship? If so, why?
4. Are you indecisive about everything?
5. Is your love motivated by selfishness?
6. Are you possessive and jealous?
7. Are you over-sensitive and defensive?
8. Must you be told many times that you are loved?
9. Do you associate love with maudlin sentimentality?
10. Is it genuine love, sexual desire, or both?
11. Have you fallen in love many times?
12. Do you feel that you can never fall in love again?
13. Do you use baby talk during lovemaking?
14. Must your love be fortified with material security?
15. Do you trust the person you love?
16. Do you believe in love at first sight?
17. Can you distinguish between "like" and "love"?
18. Must you resort to alcoholic beverages before you can love?

19. Do you have a stronger desire to be loved than
    to love?
20. Do you possess normal self-love or do you dislike
    yourself?

● *Love Controls Fear and Hate*

In the world today racial psychologies, group clannishness,
and political philosophies divide men into hostile camps. Their
members feel threatened. *Hating* the rest of the world, they
believe the answer to their *fears* lies in imposing their philosophy on the rest of the world, conquering and ruling by *war*,
if necessary.

The normal man will not allow himself to become con-
taminated by the fears and hates of another individual, of
society. The man who has learned to appreciate life for its
own sake will face its imperfections without becoming prey
to despair.

The wise man knows that he cannot stop rain, but he can
protect himself from it. He cannot fail to see that—along with
the good—hate, corruption, hypocrisy, and cynicism abound
in our society. He knows that he cannot stop wars already
under way. But he can protect his serenity from those who
would make him cynical. He can spread his own measure of
good will.

After twenty-two years of psychiatric practice, I am of the
opinion that the ills of the world are caused not only by *fear*
and *hate* but also by *love-frustrations*. *Love-sickness* is at the
root of suicides, crimes, and nervous and mental disorders
(excluding of course those caused by organic conditions).
Only with better understanding of love and its power can we
hope to reduce the imperfections of human conduct down to
a minimum.

● *The Omnipotence of Love*

The power of good will, of man's instinct to love, is not a
matter of conjecture. It is demonstrated every day. We set
it in full force when a smaller group defends a homeland

against overwhelming odds. We see it activate men who
perform almost unbelievable rescues when other men are in
danger of losing their lives. This is the force that unites
people who confront a common disaster—and invests each
man with the strength of all.

● *Developing the Capacity to Love*

Everyone is *born* with the capacity to love. Love isn't
something that just happens. Love is something that is
developed. It is part of the instinct of self-preservation. Love-
hunger is *universal.* Everyone wants to be loved. To live
is to love. To love is to live.

Some people find it difficult to *express* love because of inner
conflicts that result in loneliness and unhappiness. Others
are unable to *accept* love for the same reason. Persons who
have too much self-love (narcissism) find it difficult to love;
and those who do not possess enough self-love, who are dissatisfied with themselves, also experience difficulty in expressing love.

To illustrate, one of Dr. Theodor Reik's patients said to
him: "I cannot love because I am not pretty." Dr. Reik makes
the following comment:

> This young girl certainly over-estimated physical
> attractiveness, even apparently thinking sometimes
> that it was the only quality of value in the eyes of
> young men. What she meant was: "I know I am not
> pretty. When I am tempted to fall in love I feel at
> the start that the man won't be attracted to me.
> Thus I shall know only unhappiness and frustration.
> I can't risk falling in love because I foresee with pain
> that my feelings will not be reciprocated."[1]

● *You Must Feel Love to be Loved*

Marilyn Monroe, according to columnist Lydia Lane, is
reported to have once told the press, "When I walk I always
think 'up in front' and 'down in back.' " But the way you
carry yourself is influenced by the way you feel inside. You
must *feel* attractive to be attractive. The basis of sex appeal

---

[1] Dr. Theodor Reik, *A Psychologist Looks at Love* (New York: Farrar &
Rhinehart, 1944).

is your enjoyment of being a woman, and that means your enjoyment of being admired by the opposite sex.

"Sometimes a very attractive looking girl is not popular. Without being aware of it she has carried over from her childhood an unfriendly attitude toward boys. She may not be conscious of this but she is still fighting the battle of the sexes."

The above is applicable to the problem of love. We can paraphrase some of Miss Monroe's wise statements by saying, the way you love is influenced by the way you feel inside. You must feel love to love or be loved.

● *Love Is Unselfish*

In another instance a *selfish* and *immature* husband was responsible for blocking the capacity to love in his wife.

A young woman five years married, was sent to me as a direct result of a miserable start in married life. She had been to doctor after doctor for treatment of various chronic conditions. She suffered from fatigue, headaches, inertia, and a host of other ills. She wept easily.

Her husband, an ignorant man, did nothing but rail at her for running up doctors' bills. Various doctors had given up trying to effect a cure, and the last one she had gone to recommended psychiatry. The husband threw up his hands in disgust. "It's always something—doctors, specialists, for everything. Feet to head—now its psychiatry."

Nevertheless, she came, and in an early session she told how her husband had acted on their wedding night. He had behaved like an animal. He never once said he loved her nor asked her if she was happy. Without any preliminary lovemaking he had a quick and brutal satisfaction for himself, then rolled over and went to sleep.

Her honeymoon had started in pain, fear, and disillusionment, and she regretted the marriage. She had loved her husband, but his conduct prevented her from demonstrating her love. In tears she said, "Doctor, if my husband had been a little kinder, if he'd made love to me, talked to me—I know I could have shown him my love for him."

• How to Love, Accept Love, and Hold Love

If you want to learn to love, to accept love, to hold love when you have found it, keep in mind the following. In essence they contain the *wisdom* of the old philosophers, the *conclusions* of modern psychologists, and the sentiments of those who have *lived* and *loved successfully*. You will discover that love for you has taken on a *new meaning*.

1. Everyone is *born* with the instinct to love. Everyone should *understand* the nature of love.

2. *Real love* is *positive*. It is strong but not possessive. It is tolerant but not dependent. This is true of all real love, regardless of whether it be the love of a mother for her child, the love between members of a family or between a husband and wife; the love of the inanimate, of nature and of beauty.

3. A common denominator of all aspects of love is the *love of life itself*. It is the parent of all other forms of love, for it is like the great trunk which has many branches, all nourished by the same roots. Call it survival love—the love to endure, the love to tolerate, the love to go on and to help others. This love is gratitude for the privilege of surviving.

4. Puritanical or neurotically prudish attitudes toward sex hampers one's capacity for love. Sex can be a gesture of love. It is the spirit behind the relationship that counts. And, although the physical aspect of marriage naturally tapers off as the years pass, there is no reason for not continuing other manifestations of love. The warmth, the closeness, and the demonstrations of love can be kept alive even during those later years when the sexual act itself is not consummated. Retirement from love is bad. A kiss, the clasp of hands, a look that tokens mutual understanding—these are the gestures of love that should never be abandoned.

5. If you wish to be loved—*be lovable*. *To love is to be loved*. It is the *golden key* to love. To love also is to overcome *self-dislike*.

6. The importance of parental obligations regard-

ing the enlightenment of children about the meaning of love cannot be overemphasized. Parents of prospective brides would be wise to stress the fact that sex and marriage can be an expression of love and devotion, and that prudery is a barrier not only to sex fulfillment but also to sex enjoyment.

7. Parental compatibility and a wholesome atmosphere in the home are just as essential to the child's development of a capacity to love as rest, good food, and fresh air.

Dr. Stekel warns us: "Our fate is decided in the first years of our life. All that we learn later is but a superstructure built upon the first impressions and experiences. A well-balanced union will foster well-balanced children. The atmosphere of happiness, contentment and harmony is transferred to the child in invisible ways." He later goes on to say, "An indescribably sweet breeze blows over the friendships of childhood. They are tender, pale blue petals that tremble with each stir of the childish soul and whose roots even then already penetrate down to the deep layers in which inherited instincts and tempting desires fertilize the soil of the passions."

8. If you have been previously disillusioned, lost your love, or had your marriage culminated in a final divorce, remember that you have a *right to love again*.

9. To *say* you love someone is not enough. Love must be *felt* and demonstrated in an action of some kind. There must be *proof* of love. Words are quite often deceptive. It's deeds, not words that count. Marriage must contain *evidence* of the "Love, Honor, and Cherish" clause.

10. Love is associated with an endless longing to be with the other person. A desire to *share* the beauty and ecstacies of life—a mutual contentment. Real love is finding security in each other.

11. Love involves *successful forgetting* and *forgiveness*—a tolerance of each other's weaknesses and faults.

12. Love cannot *grow* unless it is kept *alive*.

13. Lovableness must first be found *within yourself* before you can find it in others. You cannot make a recluse of yourself and hope to find love.

14. *Advice to men:* Women feel more insecure than men. Therefore they have a greater need to be loved, a greater need to feel important, to belong, and to be needed.

15. *Advice to women:* Men need to be flattered. They wish to be *appreciated* as a lover, and they prefer women who are *responsive.* Their ego-gratification includes the satisfaction and realization that they are *also* loved.

16. Remember that *good health may* add years to your *life,* but *love* adds *life* to your years. In this atomic age, in this world that is everchanging and unpredictable, *love* is the only real security we have. We need to realize that the potentialities of love are greater than the potentialities of atomic energy.

Session 22.

~~~~~~

Plan for
Well Balanced Living

"Here's to health, happiness, and success." You've heard this toast many times. Why? Because it represents the *alpha* and *omega* of what everyone desires out of life.

If one enjoys *good health,* he is more apt to be *happy;* and, if he's *happy,* he is more likely to *succeed.*

The attainment of these three basic ingredients depends to a large extent upon the kind of planning you do.

The Master Formula:

PLAN YOUR LIFE.

WORK YOUR PLAN.

To plan is to *accomplish.* To accomplish is to *succeed.* Success feeds *happiness.*

What is happiness but a *way of living. Intelligent planning* is the *via regia* to well-balanced living.

Write down your plans on paper. Should your plans of life suddenly be blocked by something unforeseen, what then? You simply make *new ones* to fit your altered circumstances. No plan should be so *inflexible* that it prevents making a *new* plan to meet a changed situation.

237

A civil engineer builds his bridge according to the specifications of his blueprints. Progress in this world is dependent upon careful planning.

Successful living is both an *art* and a *science*. Since science is defined as "organized facts," the *science* of intelligent living can be defined as the wise application of *organized plans* that deal with a style of life—a system or technique of living, conducive to better health, increased happiness, and greater success.

Here is a *six point plan for well-balanced living*. You can modify it, make substitutions, or use it to pattern a plan of your own.

• Health-Intelligence

"Health is our life," wrote Rabelais. "Without health life is not life."

The policy of a *sound* mind in a *sound* body, as you learned, dates back to the wisdom of the Romans—*Mens sana in corpore sano*.

The following are *health-builders* that can serve as a foundation for intelligently planned living.

• Body Health

1. Eating. Proper food is essential to good physical health. Neurotics either eat too little (*anorexia nervosa*—nervous lack of appetite) or eat too much (*frustration-eating*). Most fat people are *emotionally immature*. They suffer from *mental fatness*. One of the major causes of mental sluggishness is *over-eating*. Dr. H. M. Marvin, past president of the American Heart Association, claims that "Every pound of excess weight that you carry makes it necessary for your heart to pump blood through more than three miles of blood vessels that it would not have to serve otherwise."

2. Sleep. It is estimated that approximately 52 per cent of our population suffer from *insomnia*—that each year more than three billion sleeping pills are sold. To cure yourself of insomnia you must start by not *reminding* yourself that you *cannot* fall asleep. The *fear* of not being able to go to sleep in itself will keep you awake. Good sleep is conducive to body and mind health. Everyone needs an average of six to eight hours of sleep each night. Adopt the habit of going to bed at about the same time each night. Look forward to going to bed. Put yourself into the proper *mood* for sleep.

3. Exercise. Physical indolence plays a major role in determining the expectancy of your life. Most of us *under-exercise*. The right kind of exercise, in moderation, improves circulation and physical efficiency by restoring the tonicity of fatigued muscles and maintaining the symmetry of physique. The average business or professional man of middle years returns home in the evening, enjoys a substantial dinner, turns on his TV, smokes his after-dinner cigar, and soon falls asleep, snatching at the headlines of his newspaper. His lungs need fresh air, his body wants for exercise, and his mind craves amusement. His stomach becomes the victim of his appetite for rich foods. Poor circulation and faulty elimination give him that end-of-the-day toxic feeling. Our typical middle-aged man complains of a headache and general fatigue and rationalizes for declining recreational engagements by explaining: "I must be getting old."

4. Alcohol and Tobacco. Excessive drinking and smoking come under the same category as excessive eating. Practically all chain-smokers and alcoholics ultimately suffer from health complications. Moderation is the keynote to wise living.

5. Personal-Hygiene. Keeping yourself clean boosts your morale. Morning cold showers will give you a feeling of exhilaration and well-being and improve your circulation. Warm tub baths before going to bed relax tired muscles and induce sleep. Water (*hydrotherapy*) is inexpensive. There is never an excuse for uncleanliness. Good personal hygiene also includes the development of good living habits, such as personal grooming, tidiness, and neatness, which promote proper self-respect and self-love.

6. Physical Check-up. A wise person sees his dentist twice a year and requests a complete periodic physical examination from his physician. He is educated to the importance of keeping physically fit. Many chronic illnesses, including cancer and heart disorders, might be prevented if more people developed the good health habit of consulting their doctor at frequent intervals. An annual check-up should be a "must" for every person past the age of fifty.

7. *Mind-Health.* In order to keep emotionally and mentally fit, it is imperative to overcome the *worry habit.* Worry, as you know, is a *health-destroyer*—a form of self-torment. Worry, not work, shortens life. Learn not to make mountains out of mole hills. The famous Dejerine of Paris said, "In our lives there are mountains and mole hills, but in the lives of neurasthenics there are only mountains."

When I speak of "Worry" I am referring to *excessive* worry. *Everybody* worries. Only the *dead* have no worries.

Remind yourself, *"don't hurry,"* and *"don't worry."* Mind-health implies *mind-relaxation.* Convince yourself that your physical vitality is dependent upon the kind of thinking you do. Learn to understand yourself, the nature of your personality, your fears and anxieties. Sooner or later you must come face to face with your reflected self. There is no use trying to run away. Where you go, your mind goes. If you do faulty thinking in New York, you will undoubtedly indulge in faulty thinking in New Mexico. If you are jealous in Rhode Island, you'll probably be jealous in Texas. People take their complexes with them wherever they go. Mental hygiene, like money, has value any place in the world.

Just as your mind can make you *sick,* so also can your mind make you *well.*

Prophylactic mind-health means surrendering disturbing thoughts, self-imposed handicaps, giving your mind the same attention and care as your body. Just as the body needs exercise, the mind needs to be stimulated with new interests.

You are rich or poor according to the wealth or poverty of your mind. Feed your mind with inspirational thinking as you would fill your stomach with wholesome food.

A sense of humor is essential to mental health. Everyone needs to laugh. The old philosophers knew this when they concluded that "A merry heart doeth good like medicine."

To maintain mind-health it is necessary to correct faulty attitudes and eliminate undesirable personality-traits (which can be changed at will).

Take time out from each busy day to repeat to yourself:

I am *improving* every day.
I am *growing* every day.
I am becoming *wiser* every day.
I am becoming more *mature.*
I am learning to *relax.*
I am developing greater *self-confidence.*
I *believe* in myself.
I am developing greater *peace of mind.*
I *can* be *happier.*
I *am happier.*

This technique of *autosuggestion* — defined by William J. Fielding as "the subconscious realization of an idea which tends to transform itself into action"—is based on the principle that what you tell yourself *persistently* enough you will eventually *believe* and will come to pass in your life. Try it. You'll discover it can influence your entire future.

A similar method is that of *Autoconditioning.* Dr. Hornell Hart, Professor of Sociology at Duke University, recently wrote a book on the subject, *Autoconditioning: The New Way to a Successful Life.*[1] He presents a simple workable technique of overcoming emotional difficulties—improving one's personality. Autoconditioning is based on scientific principles and is of value to those seeking self-help.

Work-Success

Work-success is usually deserved. Persons who are *lazy* are *addicts* to pipe-dreams of success. They fail to realize that

[1] Dr. Hornell Hart, *Autoconditioning: The New Way to a Successful Life.* Englewood Cliffs, N. J.: Prentice-Hall, Inc., 1956.

success is a step by step process, that it entails *ambition, determination,* and *perseverance.* It was Edison who was credited with saying "Success is 99 percent *perspiration* and 1 percent *inspiration."*

The ability to be self-supporting, to find satisfaction in work of some kind, is essential to well-balanced living.

We all need to work, whether we like it or not. Even millionaires find they have to work, mentally, if not physically, to maintain their fortunes.

People who devote the bulk of their lives to work that seems like drudgery or who work at a job that is dull should find comfort in knowing that they are at least earning an honest living and are making themselves useful. According to Dr. William S. Walsh, in an article "You And Your Job," "The vast majority of the 50,000,000 persons gainfully employed in normal times, have no enthusiasm for their work."

It takes all kinds of people for all kinds of jobs. We can't all be college professors, research scientists, or bank presidents. If possible it is naturally better to find the kind of work you are best suited for, *work that you like.* But changing jobs may not be the answer. You may have to change *yourself* and your *attitude* toward your job.[2] Those persons who makes a sincere effort to *improve* themselves by knowledge or experience generally get the "better job." They don't sit around waiting for the "breaks." Reminding yourself how much you hate your work only brings on mental exhaustion.

Stop *fighting* your job. If you can create satisfaction in your work, you are less apt to be tired and bored. The truck driver who enjoys having an outside job, the mail carrier who likes people, the store-keeper who enjoys pleasing his customers—all experience an inward satisfaction. They are fortunate insofar as they have the ability to counterbalance the monotony of their work.

Doing merely what is required of us is not enough if we want to achieve success. Elmer Wheeler in his book *The*

---

[2] Read *How to Enjoy Work and Get More Fun Out of Life, by O. A. Battista,* Englewood Cliffs, N. J.: Prentice-Hall, 1957.

Wealth Within You[3] informs us that "the outstanding person in any line does more than is required. It is that 'something extra' — the extra effort, the extra service, the extra knowledge, the extra push — that makes a champion a champion."

He adds: "If you feel that you have to do so much work because that is required of you, your work becomes a chore that gets you down. But if you feel that you want to do not only what is required, but something additional, you do what must be done with zest."

All human beings need to find something they can do. Like love, work is *medicine*. It alleviates the ills of the soul.

Success in life is not altogether a matter of fame or fortune. It is something more than *material-success*. A so-called "successful man" (in the eyes of the public) can prove a *failure* as a *lover, husband, father,* or *citizen* in his community. Success in one sphere does not necessarily imply success in all other spheres of living. However, a man who achieves work-success is more apt to be successful in other fields as well.

By the same token, a man who repeatedly experiences *work-failure,* who is a poor provider, is more apt to blame others for his own deficiencies. He is much more difficult to live with. I have encountered many neurotic people who were afraid to accept a promotion. They were afraid to assume the responsibilities of the new job. It required considerable encouragement on my part to get them to accept the better job. Many people need to be *pushed* toward success.

It is only natural to assume that most women respect men who are successful. Success is a symbol of *self-confidence*. *Confidence* makes one *happy*. A *happy* person makes *others* happy.

Work-success is just as essential to the happiness of women. Managing a home, raising children, encouraging a husband, represent *important* work. A woman succeeds or fails in her job as a wife and as a mother. Her job-success is dependent

---

[3] Elmer Wheeler, *The Wealth Within You.* Englewood Cliffs, N. J.: Prentice-Hall, Inc., 1955.

on the wisdom she exercises in knowing how to make herself happy, make her husband happy, and make her children happy.

Work-success, therefore, can be defined as the satisfaction of knowing that whatever you are doing you are doing your best — that you are working at something that is not in conflict with your conscience, that your work is not entirely selfishly motivated. Work-success does not necessarily mean material success — an obsessional drive for money and power. By work-success, I refer particularly to people who *first* achieve inner success as a *person,* (*maturity* and *personality-integration*) and who *then* find satisfaction in the work they are doing.

Next to work-success, every person needs a satisfactory love-life.

Love-Happiness

Love-success is as important in a life-program of well-balanced living as *work-success.* One can compare the need *to love* and to *be loved* to the hands of a clock. What would life be without love?

Love-happiness comes from *within.* You must have a *will to love.* Love-happiness comes from the *unselfish giving* and *receiving* of love. Love begets love. Emotional insecurity results from *love-deprivation.* Persons who feel *insecure* emotionally usually lack the capacity to give love. Others *fear* love. They cannot *accept* love in a *mature* way. Pathological jealousy, the cancer of all love relationships, causes emotional insecurity.

To love properly it is essential to control unhealthy emotions. You cannot hope to achieve love-success if you manifest a disagreeable disposition or exhibit a bad temper. To be *happy in love* you have to keep the husband-wife relationship *congenial.* Emotional wounds selfishly inflicted on each other through thoughtlessness leave lasting *scars* that *detract* from the beauty of the love-relationship.

Many disillusioned couples fail to appreciate the fact that two people have to work toward keeping the marriage happy.

Happiness isn't just something you take for granted. You need to remind yourself everyday to be congenial, unselfish and considerate. When a husband and wife begin to bicker and quarrel, they are already starting to *unmarry*.

Love-happiness and sexual harmony are allied. Sex compatibility in marriage is the cement between the bricks of love. The husband and wife who are sexually well-mated are more inclined to experience love-happiness. *Sexality* (if I may be permitted to coin a new term) referring to *personality with sex appeal*, helps keep marriage a *life-long honeymoon*.

Impotence and frigidity are less prevalent among couples who experience a feeling of true love for each other, who are aware of the importance of cultivating a personality that makes them sexually attractive. Too many men and women lack *sexality*. Persons who are affectionate by nature need no invitation to demonstrate their love for each other. They talk the same language of love.

To achieve love-happiness you must take an inventory of your personality and purge yourself of those handicaps that make for unhappy *interpersonal* relationships.

Personality-Compatibility

• *Getting Along With Yourself*

Do you have a personality problem? There is a solution to every problem. Study the facts, and the right answer will emerge. It's possible that *you* may be the problem. Subject yourself to a self-examination of your faults. Analyze them. Find out how you got that way. It is only logical that if you cannot get along with yourself you will have trouble getting along with others.

Anyone can *change* his personality for the better if he really wants to. Try it. Keep a weekly written record of your efforts and progress.

Don't get discouraged. Despair means becoming depressed, and this in turn affects those around you.

Realize that we *all* have personality problems. Day-to-day living is a problem. We are constantly confronted with chang-

246 PLAN FOR WELL BALANCED LIVING

ing situations. You have been taught by now that it is not the problem itself that is so baffling, but the manner in which you attempt to solve your particular problem — your *personal reaction* to what happens to you that is important.

Become fit company for yourself, and you are fit company for others.

● *Getting Along With Others*

In living a well-adjusted life you need to develop a *congenial* personality. It is one of the secrets of getting along with other people. Be what you expect others to be. The ability to meet and mingle with people has a definite *emotional* value.

The following are some *personality-traits* that are sure to make you *unpopular* — make you *lose* friends quickly. Avoid them.

- ☐ Selfishness
- ☐ Sarcasm
- ☐ Excessive health-complaining
- ☐ Conceit
- ☐ Frugality
- ☐ Over-aggressiveness
- ☐ Stubbornness
- ☐ Excessive criticism
- ☐ Shifting moods
- ☐ Unreasonable jealousy
- ☐ Emotional immaturity
- ☐ Vulgarity and bad manners
- ☐ Irritability
- ☐ Over-sensitiveness
- ☐ Excessive shyness
- ☐ Dishonesty
- ☐ Argumentativeness
- ☐ Untidiness
- ☐ Tactlessness
- ☐ Bad Temper
- ☐ Lack of appreciation
- ☐ Unadaptability

If you are sincerely interested in getting along with others, here are some *personality-reminders:*

√ Develop a sense of humor. Most people like to laugh. When they laugh, they feel better.

√ Compliment people more. Who doesn't like to be flattered and admired? We are all seeking recognition of one kind or another — a pat-on-the-back.

√ Show a genuine interest in other people. Remember their first and last names. Ask questions. Listen more. Talk less about yourself. When you do talk, make your conversation *stimulating*.

√ Think before you speak. People expect you to be tactful. Become a diplomat. It never pays to be sarcastic. There may be *expensive* repercussions. Over-sensitive people in many respects are like a "cracked glass." A harsh word carelessly spoken is all that is necessary to "break" them (to drive them to suicide).

√ Avoid unconstructive criticism and argumentativeness.

√ Stop being a know-it-all. Braggers annoy people. At the same time don't belittle yourself. Having a poor opinion of yourself (self-depreciation) is also *neurotic*.

√ Act mature (even if you have to put on an act).

√ Don't burden other people with your private troubles.

√ Don't be overaggressive and domineering.

√ Act friendly. You can't expect to win friends with a sour disposition.

√ Become tolerant, understanding, and considerate of everyone, always. Live and let live.

√ Control your temper.

√ Develop the art of being unselfish. Do things for other people.

√ Keep yourself physically attractive, and emotionally congenial.

Recreational Relaxation

Recreation and rest are to the body and mind what food and fresh air are to the stomach and lungs. *Life is to be enjoyed.* All work and no play tips the scales the wrong way. We all need periodic vacations. Make recreational pursuits recreation. The golfer who is over-anxious and score-conscious is not benefiting from recreational-relaxation. The impatient fisherman who becomes tense because the fish aren't biting is in the same predicament. This includes the bridge player who allows himself to become emotionally disturbed because his partner plays the wrong card.

There is no tonic so heartening to a man as the knowledge that he is earning his right to enjoy life. To enjoy life you must cultivate a sincere desire to live fully and completely. Go after what you want in life, but after you get it be sure to *enjoy* it.

Learn to let go — make life *easier* for yourself. Create your own holidays. Enrich your life with spare-time hobbies. Laugh a little bit every day. "Laughter," says Donald Laird, the psychologist, "massages the heart, increasing the rate of its beats and the force of the beats. Hence, the phrase 'hearty laughter'."

Head-workers especially need recreational-relaxation. When you relax you work better and feel better. In learning to relax you must be patient. People who are nervous and high-strung are very impatient, always in a hurry, and consequently suffer from an inability to relax. They are preoccupied with worrisome thoughts that counteract any effort to relax.

Fear causes tension, which in turn tightens muscles. To relax you must let your muscles go limp. *Muscle-relaxation* produces *mind-relaxation*. Relaxation benefits everyone. When you relax you become less afraid. Dentists have discovered that patients who relax experience less pain. When you relax also, people around you begin to relax *(psychic-contagion)*. Just as tension, fear, hostility and irritability are contagious, so is laughter, friendliness, and relaxation.

Conscience-Religion

"Conscience" may be defined as an *inner religion* found in *all* human beings. No man is born without a *"conscience,"* which psychoanalysts refer to as the *"super-ego"* component of our mind.

A conscience-religion is not a *punitive* religion. It is a *soul-satisfying philosophy* — one to live by. It is an *everyday-religion* based on *ethical precepts* — a religion of tomorrow — spiritual wisdom allied with modern psychology and practical common sense. Not all churchgoers have a conscience-religion. Its basic concept incorporates the idea of a purpose to living, a faith in a Power greater than man, an appreciation of the wonders of the universe, *a joy of existence.*

What is your philosophy of life? Did you ever try to formulate one? Everyone needs to put down on paper what he believes about everything — life, people, religion. Try it. You may discover much about yourself — the *why* of yourself.

A person who has conscience-religion has *soul-health.* He is not materialistic. He is not a slave to fanatic idealism. He neither lives in an ivory tower, nor is a victim of a distorted sense of values. He is not a fatalist, believing that what is meant to be will be. He has no conflicts with his church-religion. *Soul-health* is as essential as *body-health* and *mind-health.*

Conscience-religion fosters *human understanding, growth of personality, unselfishness,* and *serenity* through *freedom from guilt, anxiety, and "sin"; freedom from self-hate, freedom from neurotic self-denial* and *self-condemnation, freedom from a fear of God, freedom from a fear of the "devil."* It acknowledges the imperfections and frailties of human nature, enables us to develop a *realistic* understanding of their origin, and inspires a desire for a more *positive* way of living.

Conscience-religion means the attainment of *emotional maturity* — an appreciation of the wisdom of treating our fellow-man in the same manner as we would want him to treat us — (*a principle of ethics* that constitutes the common denominator of all traditional religions) — a realization that our *conscience is our own psychiatrist.*

$\mathcal{E}$pilogue

A Closing Thought

Now that our 22 sessions of psychotherapy have come to an end, let me impart this closing thought. It is not what you already know or have recently learned from this book or any other book that is important, but it is how you manage to apply this newly acquired knowledge to day-to-day living that is *really* important.

Insight *per se* is not the complete answer. It requires the *wise application of helpful insight, effective self-discipline* and *constructive action* to achieve well-balanced living.

Knowledge becomes *wisdom* only after it has been put to practical use.

The value you will have derived from these sessions will be obtained by *what you intend to do about yourself*, how much you have learned about your *real self*, the extent to which you have resolved inner conflicts, and your ability to follow directions.

As Albert E. Cliffe, author of *Lessons in Successful Living* [1] stated: "When you purchase a package of seeds you find the directions printed on the cover, and you know that if you sow those seeds according to the directions you will get the results you desire. If however, you plant those seeds in some way

---

[1] Albert E. Cliffe, *Lessons in Successful Living*. Englewood Cliffs, N. J.: Prentice-Hall, Inc., 1953.

not in accordance with the directions you will get no results whatsoever. Therefore in such a case you must never blame the seed house which supplied them."

A *new way of life* — healthier, happier, more successful — is *yours* if you are *willing* to make the necessary effort, if you are willing to *plan* and *work* your *plan*. As one writer expressed it:

> Men without plans are at the mercy of the vagrant winds of fortune. Men with plans and determination to follow them have control of their destiny. The choicest prizes that life has to offer go to those who make plans. The leftovers go to the aimless.

Forget *yesterday*. Live *today*.

When you awaken tomorrow morning, start your *new* day with the conviction that —

HAPPINESS IS BUT A WAY OF LIVING
and
that you *alone* hold
the *key* to happiness.

Index

252